DATE DUE

YOGA

The Way to
Long Life and Happiness

YOGA

The Way to Long Life and Happiness

DESMOND DUNNE

Principal of The School of Yoga, Surrey, England,
Founder of The School of Yoga, Evanston, Illinois,
and of Schools of Yoga in Paris, Oslo, Brussels,
Geneva, Casablanca, and Wellington

Illustrated by Erna Pinner

WILFRED FUNK · New York

3

Contents

Foreword

I KNOW the criticisms that this book will meet. They will say that it plays with philosophy. That it takes liberties with science. That it fits in nowhere.

But I am content that it should be judged by the acid test of personal trial. These things that I have recorded must necessarily challenge convention. It is only to be expected that they should belong to no orthodoxy. Yet those who test them will not find them wanting.

This book was written at the request of many students who already owe to Yogism their longer, happier life. It is a short, popular introduction to a vast, fascinating subject. As such it can only sketch an outline; but there is enough, I think, for the most skeptical to investigate. I merely ask that they do it with an open mind.

Yogism is a Life Science. Its object is to make modern living more tolerable. It claims that whatever your status, and howsoever the tides of fortune rise and fall with you, your ultimate experience of life can be conditioned by choice. Most of us injure our health, our happiness, our prospects of a long, successful career, through ignorance. We can replace that ignorance with knowledge—by the study of ourselves. Write to me if you wish further guidance and I will consider it a pleasure to help.

DESMOND DUNNE

Insight House, New Malden
Surrey, England

CHAPTER 1

Why Yogism?

LONG life and happiness! These two should always go together. One without the other is only half the necessary. Nature has no more pathetic spectacle than a miserable old man or woman. Except, perhaps, a young life cut short in the first flush of eager, expectant youth.

In an ideal order of society, men would live long and happily, retaining their full powers into ripe old age. And when I say "old age," I mean a century or more. Charles Henry Arnold, Britain's oldest man, wrote at the age of 110,

I certainly am not decrepit and helpless—I am still very active and my brain still has the quality of being able to function quite normally. My general health is excellent. You can see in me a living example of the benefits to be derived from the practice of Yoga studies, which combine the power of thought and concentration. To Yoga I attribute my longevity.

A happy long life is something we may all enjoy. *And it is never too late to begin.* If you are young now, Yoga will be a safe investment for your future. If you are old, it will be a better than average speculation. Witness these two reports from mere beginners.

At seventy, one of my students writes:

All my friends confirm the benefits I have felt and say they have noticed a remarkable change for the better in my health. I was always living at tension and never knew how to relax properly. I feel 100 per cent better now.

Another student, in his eighty-first year, reports:

I have experienced a marked improvement—so much so that it has been noted by my friends and acquaintances. A fine color and quick mentality and a general appearance of fine health. Numbers of people have remarked that I now look sixty. You have a course of lessons better than psychologists can offer, for you offer what they can and more than they can. It is marvelous.

One would think, judging from many modern reference books, that man knew nothing about his personality until the dawn of twentieth-century psychology. But the struggle to wrest from Nature the secret of long life and happiness is no new undertaking. It is ageless. Naturally, in these materialistic times, it has assumed a materialistic form. New "miracle" drugs are now announced and exposed with monotonous regularity.

New forms of injection and gland therapy likewise enjoy their brief fashion. Modern medicine is doing fine in this direction, but the most powerful stimulants still seem fated to have only an ephemeral effect. Drugs and injections give life an extra flicker but invariably there is relapse. They cannot be relied upon to extend and deepen our grasp of life.

No, if men would prolong their days and fill to overflowing their cup of happiness, drugs and gland-grafting will not help them. They must look elsewhere for an elixir. The age-old science of Yoga bids them look *within*. Those who have reached the sixties are still, it says, in the springtime of youth. Yogis in the East know how to prolong life long past the span of a hundred years, retaining their mental and physical powers undiminished. What they can do, so also can we.

Sooner or later, we of the West must abandon for good the cruel, stupid idea of being "too old at forty." Common sense has already refuted it, but the superstition lingers in the "Help Wanted" columns. Yet until a man or woman has reached the forties, his or her experience of life is bound to be limited and uncoordinated. It takes forty years or more to rub the corners off a sensitive personality. It is unquestionable that we are then in better shape to serve our fellow creatures.

All civilized life is a struggle against death and misery. Any system which can lengthen our years and increase our happiness must therefore repay investigation. Yoga claims to do both these things. Not surprisingly, then, it is inspiring great interest among Western peoples. They are influenced partly by curiosity, partly by the vague feeling that this ancient philosophy has something important to teach them. Unfortunately, serious investigations are few. To the vast majority, Yoga remains an unknown quantity.

The most curious notions prevail as to what the word itself implies, no doubt due to the antics of stage performers. Under the pretense of "demonstrating" Yoga, these gentry stick pins into their flesh, lie on beds of nails, or insist on being photographed standing on their heads. Needless to say, this kind of showmanship has no connection with genuine Yoga, a subject of serious study for at least 3,000 years.

This book is, however, about *Yogism*, a modern adaptation of ancient Yogic facts and theories. This adaptation is designed to help civilized people to lengthen and enrich their days. It is an attempt to orient an age-old tradition so that it may be understood and applied by people living today. However, before introducing Yogism as such, we should first examine our source material. A clear definition of the word *Yoga* is imperative. Literally it means *union,* but more simply it can be described as a process of self-education. It shows how, by the study of our own moods and emotions, we may enter into possession of perfect health, achieve greater mental and physical control, and gain more control of our own destiny.

The early Upanishads (Oriental scriptures) defined Yoga in the English sense of Yoke or Union with God. Later commentators, notably Bhoja, taught quite the opposite—*dis*union, *e.g.*, a greater extension of the Self. So it seems that Yoga, in its traditional form, involved either Self-realization or God-realization, according to the practitioner's attitude.

These fine speculations may appear idle to the canny Western mind, more interested in immediate practical benefits. A good many readers will not be particularly anxious for "union with God." They will be more immediately concerned to escape their stomach ulcers, blood pressures, complexes, and frustrations. And it must be admitted that philosophy is a poor poultice for a pain in the abdomen, nor will it pay your debts. Life's hard "facts," as we call them, require that they be faced realistically. We must come down to earth.

Which is one reason why traditional forms of Yoga (consisting as they do, of obscure and abstract theories) need to be restated and adapted. Otherwise, the long life and happiness which Yoga undoubtedly offers will continue to evade our grasp.

Most popular, certainly, of all traditional forms of Yoga is that known as the *Hatha* system. Its object is to achieve complete control over the physical organism. Disciples are taught how to suppress all voluntary and involuntary activity—even to control the autonomic nervous system, a seemingly impossible feat. That it is not impossible they have demonstrated by being buried alive, completely suspending all breathing movements, halting the heart beats, the peristaltic motions of the intestines, and so on—master proof, it seems to me, of the power of mind over matter.

Obviously, such attainments are not everybody's ambition. In fact, their performance entails such severe disciplines that the ordinary Westerner would find them intolerable.

Originally, the whole object of Hatha Yoga was to prepare the body for spiritual development. That—and that alone—justified this astonishing physical control. But the initial target has been lost to sight in modern times, even among Oriental exponents. Many present-day Hatha Yogis mistake the means for the end. Their achievements explain the amazing stories told by visitors just home from India. Even allowing for the fakes, shams, and charlatans, whose number is legion, there is unquestionable proof of "miracles" performed by genuine Hatha Yogis. Their immunity to pain, their ability to suppress physical sensation, is astounding—but it was first taught as a stepping-stone to higher, spiritual development. The original Hatha Yogis pledged themselves to be nonviolent in their actions, to tell the absolute truth at all times, never to steal, to be chaste in all their thinking, and to free themselves of all worldly possessions. Their entire training had a spiritual objective. In their search for purity and contentment, they practiced the utmost austerity. Thus, their bodies were purified to receive what Christians would call the Holy Spirit.

Another Yoga system, known as *Bhakti,* is based almost entirely on devotional practices. Its adherents seek happiness through the pursuit of love and worship. Their ideas have consequently a strong emotional basis. This distinguishes them again from the *Janana* Yogis, who develop extreme discrimination and self-analysis through prolonged feats of concentration and meditation.

More practical, to our way of thinking, is the system known as *Karma Yoga*—the path of action. Members of this group win their happiness and long life by performing unselfish deeds and cultivating an attitude of complete nonattachment to material rewards. In the words of the Bhagavad-Gita, they "renounce attachment to the fruits, and are indifferent to the results, of all actions, present and future, praise and blame equally."

The peak of Yoga systems is reached in *Raja Yoga,* and is far above the grasp of any Western explorer. Raja Yoga incorporates something of each of the other methods—and a great deal more besides. Above all, it aims at gaining full control of one's fleeting moods and emotions. The exponent is taught to shut off thought as simply and deliberately as we should press an electric-light button. He learns to withdraw completely from all worldly associations. Feeling and thought are completely short-circuited as he reaches the state of *samadhi* or perfect bliss. In this condition, he believes that his consciousness becomes absorbed in the Infinite, and thus he passes his days in endless bliss.

There are other refinements of these basic systems of Yoga. For example, *Mantra Yoga,* by which sensitivity is increased through the repetition of certain mystical affirmations; *Kundalini Yoga,* which teaches a technique for awakening dormant nervous energy; and *Laya Yoga,* based on abstinences, sense-withdrawal, and deep concentration until, finally, the disciple merges his consciousness in God.

From the foregoing it will be evident that the word *Yoga* has a multiplicity of interpretations. It will also be clear that none of the traditional systems can be seriously followed under normal civilized conditions. The demands and disciplines are so severe and so sweeping that any such attempt would be only misguided and foolish. Moreover, each system presumes the attendance of a personal *Guru* (or teacher) for the *Chela* or disciple. The *Chela* must dedicate his whole life to Yoga study.

Even in the East, genuine Gurus are few in number. Alas, many who endow themselves with this ancient and honored title are merely neurotics who hope, by prescribing for others' ailments, to find a vicarious escape from their own.

Every year, hundreds of devout young Indians ascend the Himalayas in search of caves and *ashrams* (schools) which the Gurus are supposed to inhabit. They return, having discovered only other students, just like themselves, also seeking the elusive Guru.

If, then, Yoga is so many-sided, and authentic instruction is so hard to come by in India its cradle, how can a Westerner hope for enlightenment? Unlike the Oriental, he has no time to make long journeys to distant retreats. He cannot waste months indulging in meditation. He has a home and family to support, a job to do, a worldly minded employer to please. His whole mode of life—its din, its slavishness, its artificiality—are quite unsuited to the serious, lifelong study which all the traditional forms of Yoga require.

A wide gulf, which no bridge can span, separates Eastern from Western living. This is, unhappily, a fact ignored by most translators of Sanskrit texts purporting to reveal the "true" Yoga. These well-intentioned authors forget that the original Sanskrit was a highly condensed and staccato language, having no affinity with modern English. The people who employed it had little in common with twentieth-century civilization. Consequently, literal translations of Sanskrit texts on Yoga can lead to very curious interpretations. You may read descriptions of Yogic postures, "lifted" from Sanskrit sources, with such peremptory claims as "This posture destroys all diseases"—a statement never intended for unqualified acceptance, when merely hinted in the Sanskrit tongue more than 2,000 years ago. "By this *Danta-Dhauti* every kind of heart disease is widely cured," another Sanskrit text has been rendered in English. "This *mudra* gives the power of levitation," runs a third. How ridiculous! As though any one physical or mental exercise could perform such wonders.

Yet Western civilization dearly needs some of the undoubted psychological benefits which follow Yogic practice. Of these, *inner peace* is, perhaps, the greatest wish. Having fought two wars, with a third on the horizon, we all share a great, instinctive longing for peace. We seek peace of mind and peace of spirit, such as the application of Yoga is said to bestow. This deep, abiding peace is elusive under modern living conditions. Even those who sneer at the ancient Yogis' preoccupation with affairs of the spirit will grant that peace is the one thing above all others which our tense, frustrated civilization craves. They may dismiss the Yogi as a poor, benighted fool; but his self-possession and happiness they must envy in their hearts.

None of us in the Western world is so independent as to be entirely free from the general impact of economic strains. The business of making a living becomes every year more competitive and irritating. All are ensnared by the dilemma it poses. "Late and

soon, getting and spending, we lay waste our powers"
—for the simple reason that there seems no other way
of life possible. With what result? A peptic ulcer,
nerves, blood pressure? Even when the body doesn't
suffer, the mind is soon unfitted to enjoy the fruits of
retirement. Many people spend a lifetime working to
amass enough money for a happy retirement. When
the knot of work is cut, they are surprised to find
themselves at a loose end. They work at top tempo
every year of their lives, dreaming of a cottage in the
country or a haven by the sea. When at last they do
have time to spare they have no idea how to employ
it. Ill health and exhaustion have taken the relish
from retirement. Long life is no boon in such circumstances, for life itself has lost its purpose.

Yet there is no reason why the average man or
woman reaching seventy should not retain a robust
physical and mental fitness and continue in possession
of the same for many years. The oriental Yogi's power
over the body proves that this can be done. The question is *how?* We cannot turn Mrs. Jones into a Hatha
Yogi—God forbid! Her body would not allow her to
perform the complicated physical postures which are
part of the Hatha Yogi's training. No more can Mr.
Smith, who during the day buys goods to resell on a
precarious profit margin, devote his evening leisure to
Raja Yoga—even were his business ethics suddenly
transformed. Indeed, if Mrs. Jones or Mr. Smith were
so misguided as to try, they would only be attempting
to live two lives at once—an impossible feat which
involves dangerous nervous unbalance.

The first thing, then, to be done by any Westerner

contemplating the study of Yoga is to abandon the idea of practicing it in traditional form. Since it is evident there is no one "authorized" system of Yoga —on the contrary, there are many conflicting traditional versions—why not have a modern system adapted to present-day Western needs? This is exactly what I myself evolved and have taught with success to several thousand students. It proves that the transition from East to West, and from ancient to modern times, can be effected. And this without the aid of the mysterious Guru! The best of all Gurus has proved to be the written word. This is the medium through which the ancient Sanskrit teachings reach out to us across the bridge of time. Moreover, the absence of a personal Guru removes one pitfall which threatens all attempting to follow the traditional Yoga path. Too many seek a Guru not for wisdom, but to gratify their inner weakness. They want him for the purpose of self-escape. Into his lap they aim to empty their cares and responsibilities—thereby making life simple and easy. But Yogism—the name given to my own version of Yoga—begins by affixing responsibility squarely on the student. He and no other can achieve his salvation. Progress depends on his personal exertions.

In short, Yogism is a synthesis of ancient Yoga teachings, adapted to present-day needs. It has been supplemented by the discoveries of modern psychology. The two blend into a unified system combining the fruits of East and West, remote times and the twentieth century.

The result is something both old and new. It was

Yoga which gave me the idea that certain unconscious actions which we all perform daily could be amplified in such a way as to increase greatly their recuperative powers. These natural functions are indispensable to human life. Without breath, you would die. Without rest, you would wear out. Without thought, you would not be conscious. And without action, you could achieve nothing.

In Yogism I have singled out these four basic human functions for special study and development because it seemed to me they provided all we need to enrich life. Each function was broken down into its component parts. Then, through close-range observation of its different elements, I was able to evolve a better living technique which has since been tested and proved by men and women of all types, ranging from the very young to what we normally regard as the very elderly. The benefits realized were, in the first place, of a physical order. That is to say, help is given in absorbing the stresses and strains of everyday living. This leads in due course to the development of greater reserves of nervous energy. And this, in turn, has enabled the individual student to widen his sphere of service to family and community. Those who apply this technique become healthier, happier citizens. They enjoy a rise in self-confidence, more control over the detail of their lives, and greater ability to cope with difficult personal problems which normally put a tax on nervous energy. Above all, vitality is increased, and ailments of many types have been relieved, if not actually removed, through a new flood tide of Self-faith.

These are admittedly bold claims. In setting them down, I realize they will be received skeptically. But I do not ask you to take them on my word. There is abundant evidence for you to examine. It can be proved that my technique of Deep Relaxation (Chapter 3) does soothe away feelings of tension and anxiety. After practicing Deep Relaxation, students invariably feel relieved and fortified; their own testimony is overwhelming. The complement of this technique is Deep Contraction (Chapter 4), a system of physical exercise which I have developed from the ancient Yogic *asanas*. This system differs fundamentally from ordinary physical culture since, unlike the latter, it does not require numerous repetitions of a given series of physical movements. In Deep Contraction a single natural and enjoyable stretch is developed and prolonged to its maximum extent. A stimulating blood-flush is thus sent to all parts of the system and a sensation of energy and freshness immediately replaces fatigue.

The next step was to develop the technique which I have called "Dynamic Breathing." I evolved this from the ancient Yogic art of *pranayama*, once again uniting traditional and modern discovery in what will one day be known as the "science of breath." Dynamic Breathing (Chapter 5) is a hitherto unexplored source of energy, which anyone may learn to tap.

Finally, my Dynamic Concentration technique (Chapter 6) brings up to date ancient research concerned with mental alertness and personal efficiency. These exercises, too, are based on close observation of the normal processes of concentration.

Now, anyone prepared to spend a little time in studying these four steps to more abundant living cannot help but prolong his life. What is no less important, he will live his increased years *more happily*. My researches show that anyone of average intelligence can experience benefit from applying the principles of Yogism. No special aptitudes are called for, nor are there any age limitations.

Civilization imposes so many irksome restrictions that few people are free to enjoy a full life, either in terms of years or personal happiness. Yet, paradoxically, just how humiliating and repressive life can become for the masses is not generally realized. So in the next chapter we shall briefly investigate the kind of life that is reported by the average person living under today's stresses and strains. With this picture we can compare the transformation experienced by persons who practice Yoga. And from this comparison we may find that, for all our modern conveniences, we busy Westerners can still learn from the East.

Our evolution has taken us on a unique path of discovery, and our achievements are mightily different from those of the Oriental. Naturally we are proud of our unparalleled scientific genius—though it is a tragedy that it always seems to point the way to war. Certainly, we have more creature comforts than the ancient philosophers dreamed. In many other ways, too, we are great, gifted, and powerful.

But it is beginning to dawn upon the West that long life and happiness—the true fundamentals of living—have escaped it. We are learning that these boons cannot be gained by scientific inventiveness.

We are learning that they cannot be imbibed from a medicine bottle nor grafted from a gland.

The ancient philosophers of the East may have been ignorant of atomic rays and all the other deadly paraphernalia developed by the wise of our day. Those ancients studied *life*—and this is a thing which we, in our wisdom, have almost forgotten: a thing which our triumphant science often ignores.

Now, if we *really* seek the life abundant, is it not clear that the sooner we repair this omission the better will be our chance of living longer and enjoying happiness?

CHAPTER 2

Western Attitudes
Toward Life

WHAT is the average man's reaction to life? *Is* he happy? *Is* he satisfied? *Does* he feel the effort worth while?

Or is he frustrated, unhappy, disillusioned?

What exactly does he feel?

I invited Mass-Observation to interview a representative cross section of the public in a London district about their reactions to life. Mass-Observation is an organization specializing in this type of mass investigation.* I felt their unique experience and skill would settle this question better than any theorizing.

Now, it is surprising how little we know about other people's lives—their inner feelings and unspoken convictions. So an intriguing and valuable piece of research along modern scientific lines was set in motion when this investigation was undertaken.

* Mass-Observation is the British equivalent of the American Institute of Public Opinion, popularly called the "Gallup Poll." —*Editor.*

Broadly speaking, the questions were framed to find out how far people are affected by the characteristic afflictions of civilized life—lack of energy, frustration, the sense of purposelessness. A supplementary question was also asked to ascertain public reaction to the word "Yoga." This question was necessary to check whether the people interviewed were, in fact, truly representative—it was important that the sample should *not* contain students of Yoga. But more of that later. First let us study the Mass-Observation report. Here it is, in that organization's own words:

In reply to the question, "Do you feel you have as much energy as you should have?", slightly more than half the people interviewed said "Yes." The proportion saying "Yes" was markedly higher among men than women, and among the younger than the higher age groups. The results may be tabulated as follows:

Enough energy	52 per cent
Not enough energy	47 per cent
Don't know	1 per cent
	100 per cent

The 47 per cent of the total sample who felt that their energy was insufficient were then asked, "What gives you the feeling that you haven't enough energy?" Some people described the symptoms which had led them to this belief—consisting usually of excessive tiredness or general debility. The majority, however, went beyond the literal wording of the question and explained what they thought were the causes of this lack of energy.

In reply to the question, "On the whole, would you say you are getting what you want out of life or not?", 56 per cent of the total sample gave a negative or doubtful answer, while 44 per cent answered in the affirmative. Women (60 per cent) were more convinced of failure than men (52 per cent).

> *Not* getting what they want out of life
>   (or doubtful)   56 per cent
> Getting what they want   44 per cent
> _____
>   100 per cent

The people who said that, on the whole, they were not getting what they wanted out of life were then asked what they considered was preventing them. Of all who were asked this second question:

> 81 per cent gave answers which may be grouped under the heading "material conditions"
> 33 per cent gave answers which may be grouped under the heading of "mental, spiritual conditions"

The 81 per cent who blamed material conditions fell into the following groups:

> 50 per cent who said "not enough money"
> 27 per cent who mentioned working, living conditions (*e.g.,* food, housing, shortages, unpleasant job)
> 4 per cent who mentioned definite ill health

Over and over again, stress was laid on the high cost of living. Frequently, answers were given which stressed both lack of money and shortages. Also included in the "living-conditions" category were some answers that blamed the government or "the system."

The answers of the 33 per cent who mentioned "mental, spiritual conditions" were not so easily grouped. Approximately, however, they fell into the following divisions:

9 per cent said lack of time, leisure, entertainment
6 per cent said family problems, responsibilities
4 per cent said failure of hopes or ambitions
4 per cent said own failings, lack of initiative
2 per cent said difficulty of personal relations
2 per cent said worry
6 per cent gave miscellaneous answers

The whole sample was next asked: "In what way, if any, do *you* feel frustrated?" The proportion of people answering "Don't know" was slightly larger than to the previous one, amounting in this case to 26 per cent. Excluding these, the answers fell into the following categories:

67 per cent mentioned, broadly speaking, material circumstances
41 per cent mentioned, broadly speaking, mental, spiritual circumstances

Of the first category—

24 per cent mentioned money
19 per cent mentioned living conditions, housing shortages, etc.
17 per cent mentioned their job
7 per cent mentioned definite ill health
————
67 per cent

Of the second category—

9 per cent mentioned personal relationships
7 per cent mentioned failure of hopes, ambitions
5 per cent mentioned boredom
4 per cent mentioned fatigue
4 per cent said "It does apply to me, but I'm not sure how."
12 per cent gave miscellaneous answers
————
41 per cent

It will be appreciated that these questions in particular produced very diverse answers, and that the more fully people reply, the more difficult it is to label their answers for statistical presentation. We therefore append a considerable number of direct quotations to help fill in the picture.

> I get fed up trying to get food and make it tasty, and then my family just eat it up and don't notice the trouble I've taken to tempt them. (HOUSE-WIFE, 57)

> I want to make a go of life. I spent twenty-five years in the army and hated it—there was nothing to do in those days, you couldn't get a job. When I came out, I put my savings into my business. Now that will go, although I've worked hard—all because of the Government. (TAXI CAB OWNER, 58)

> I'm in a soul-destroying job. I hate it, but I have to stick it for family reasons. I'd like to feel I was able to create something, it would satisfy one; I try to do so by hobbies, but it's not enough. (CIVIL SERVICE WORKER, 45)

> I don't seem to be able to reason a problem out. I can't face up to it, I keep pushing it to one side, but it comes back to me, often in the night, and I feel helpless. I think that is frustration. (HOME ECONOMICS TEACHER, 52)

> As a human being, with belief in myself as a spirit, the whole struggle of spiritual progress involves frustration, else it would be no struggle. I can never picture a moment when I am entirely free from frustration, from the inevitable nature of progress. The form alters as I alter, in principle it's always there. It is the hard soil through which new life must penetrate like a blade of grass. (CIVIL SERVICE WORKER, 47)

> I don't really know what I want, but I do want things different. I get fed up because I'm bored—

there's nothing to do. I'm not unhappy, I'm just dull. I am really happiest when I am at work. (FACTORY WORKER, 25)

I want to do more for my family but I can't— when the beer isn't strong enough—when my boss picks on me for no reason—when I can't go to sleep—when my ulcers trouble me and I get very bad-tempered and I shout at my wife and kids. I am sorry after, but I can't bring myself to say so. (NIGHTWATCHMAN, 46)

A supplementary question, "What does the word *Yoga* mean to you?" was put, designed to ascertain if the sample had any knowledge of this study. It will be seen from the table below that about half the sample had only a very rough idea of what the word signified. Approximately 36 per cent of these, or 20 per cent of all people interviewed, said that Yoga was something *foreign:*

> 44 per cent said "don't know"
> 26 per cent said a religion, religious man
> 16 per cent said a system of exercise
> 4 per cent said a system of mental and physical control
> 10 per cent gave miscellaneous answers

The age and sex composition of the people interviewed was as follows:

SEX:	49 per cent women	
	51 per cent men	
AGE:	16-24 years	16 per cent
	25-44 years	42 per cent
	45 or over	42 per cent

This ends the public-opinion analysis undertaken by Mass-Observation. It demonstrates that the average person does feel the need of some stimulus to happier living but is ignorant of Yogism as a solution. He looks instead for some new physical or material boon which might help him redress his impediments.

Is Yogism a solution? Following the investigation above described, I asked Mass-Observation to undertake a second inquiry. This was directed to results reported by people who were actually studying Yogism. In what way, if any, was *their* experience of life different from that of the average man or woman?

One thousand reports voluntarily submitted by students of the School of Yoga were accordingly analyzed. This analysis "left no doubt that the average student applying the Yogism principles is more than satisfied with the results they produce and does, indeed, feel more energetic, purposeful, and happier as a result of the study."

Here, in their own words, is Mass-Observation's second report. It proves how different life can become when seen from a new vantage point:

Our analysis showed quite clearly that almost all the Yogism students regarded the immediate effects of the Course as emphatically beneficial to them. The decided tone of most of this voluntary testimony leaves little doubt that the majority of these students was convinced that the Course was doing them good—and often a quite varied good; many were enthusiastic.

Only 1 per cent (that is, 10 out of the 1,000 reports examined) felt themselves, at the end of their training, unable to say that they had found any lessons helpful.

Besides this general willingness to concede the value of the Course, there was widespread favorable comment of the most spontaneous kind. The Yogism training was frequently praised not only for its efficiency in alleviating specific symptoms but also, more positively, for improving general bodily and mental well-being. Improvements specified ranged over a wide field.

The following extracts from Yogism students' reports are typical of large numbers testifying this way:

> I have now a clear skin, calm temper, and a belief in the future.

> The capacity of my lungs is increased, I have greater development of the chest and also improved tenacity and staying power.

> I feel fitter and happier.

> I have more patience, and I don't get so worked up.

> I have found a general improvement, such as, I can say at such a time I will do a certain task, and do it, even though the radio is on.

> I have a more buoyant feeling and my friends are beginning to remark on the color in my face, which is natural—no make-up.

Some were even more enthusiastic and felt they had experienced an improvement that was more deep-seated. Here are three examples, typical of many:

> My head feels clearer. I look and feel better than I have done for a long time past. I find that I am beginning to choose my thoughts and attitudes and am thrilled to know that from now on I needn't be a victim of depression, but know just how to sidetrack it. In this Course I am finding all that I have been seeking.

> I am definitely more calm and placid, more awake to the good things of life. I take more interest in the house and in any jobs I do.

> I feel that my natural self has begun to exert itself. My mind and body are working in peace and close harmony.

The value of the Yogism exercises seemed to lie in their immediate *physical* effects, such as increased bodily fitness, suppleness, and relaxation. The Yogism lessons, on the other hand—apart from appreciation of their general "good advice"—were valued chiefly for their guidance in achieving mind-control and concentration. But, generally, the most frequently mentioned benefit of the Course (greater bodily alertness and fitness) was a physical rather than psychological effect; and, on the whole, physical benefits seemed to be reported more frequently than mental.

At the early and middle stages of Yogism training, the most frequently mentioned physical benefit of the Yogism exercises was the feeling of relaxation or refreshment which they induced. Toward the completion of the Course, however, these effects seem to be superseded by the sense of greater physical alertness, fitness, and suppleness.

Further, out of every 100 advanced Yogism students who wrote to say they had found the exercises successful:

TABLE 1 *

28 said they felt physically more alert and fit

24 said they had lost excess fat or gained in bodily suppleness

17 said they felt physically more relaxed

11 said they had learned breathing control or easier breathing

10 said they had found relief from various ailments

4 said they had found relief from indigestion, stomach trouble, constipation, etc.

2 said they slept better or more restfully

* Percentages exceed 100 even though the table is incomplete because many people mentioned more than one type of improvement.

It should be realized that these reports and all others analyzed herewith were quite spontaneous. Had students been asked specifically whether they felt fitter or had gained relief from specific ailments, etc., it is likely, bearing in mind the volume of testimonials given spontaneously to that effect, that these percentages above would have been very much higher. As they stand, however, they are very impressive, representing, as they do, the things that came first to students' minds when reporting to the School in their studies.

Physical effects of the Yogism Lessons, on the other hand, were more frequently mentioned. Out of every 100 advanced Yoga students who wrote to say they had found the lessons helpful:

TABLE 2 *

23 said the Lessons gave them good physical advice

9 said the Lessons made them physically more alert and fit

5 said the Lessons taught them breathing control or easier breathing

5 said the Lessons made them physically more relaxed

4 said the Lessons had helped them to lose fat or gain in bodily suppleness

4 said the Lessons had brought them relief from indigestion, stomach troubles

2 said the Lessons had helped them to sleep more easily or more restfully

2 said the Lessons had brought them relief from various other ailments

* Percentages are less than 100 because many people mention mental rather than physical effects. These results should be considered in conjunction with those given in Table 4.

One third of all advanced Yogism students further spontaneously reported themselves to be physically more alert and fit, and 1 in 8 reported that they were sleeping better. Others mentioned improvements ranging from more efficient eyesight to relief from constipation and indigestion. Several said they were better at getting up in the morning. Satisfactions of this largely physical kind were very varied, but here are some examples:

> You will be surprised to learn that even at my advanced years I undertook the concreting of the garden path with 4-inch concrete alone, and turned out a good job. This I put down to the unusual strength obtained through the exercises. Next week, God willing, will start painting the outside of the bungalow.

> I definitely feel better in health, and have managed to stop smoking also. I feel as though I am a better man all round.

> My girth is reduced—the unhealthy fat round my neck and jowls is greatly reduced. I'm not nearly so tired after a day's work.

> I can leave my glasses off which I have worn for twelve years. A pain in my left breast has disappeared.

Physical rather than psychological effects were most often given as reasons underlying satisfaction with the Yogism exercises; nevertheless, there was a greater mental well-being too.

For beginners, the psychological benefits seemed to be largely a matter of increased capacity for mental relaxation and refreshment, though, toward the end of the Course, a much wider range of mental improvements was reported. Out of every 100 advanced Yogism students who said that any exercises were successful:

TABLE 3 *

8 said they had a calmer outlook
6 said they experienced more mental relaxation
5 said they had better powers of concentration and mental control
2 said they were mentally more alert and fit
2 said they felt more self-confident
1 said he felt in a more cheerful frame of mind

* These percentages add to less than 100 because they represent part only of the complete table. They should be considered in conjunction with physical results given in Table 2.

Although physical reasons were altogether more frequent than mental ones, the single most-often mentioned reason for finding the Yogism Course helpful was increased capacity for mind control and concentration. Both at the middle and end of the course, a steady *1 in 5* mentioned this result of the Yogism Lessons. Out of every 100 advanced students who found any lessons helpful:

TABLE 4 *

21 said they had better mind control and powers of concentration
6 said they felt more self-confident
5 said they felt in a calmer state of mind
3 said they had been forced to understand what they were studying
3 said they felt more mentally relaxed
2 said they felt in a more cheerful state of mind
2 said they felt exhilaration, a sense of power or vibrations

* These percentages add to less than 100 because they represent part only of the complete table. They should be considered in conjunction with physical results given in Table 2.

More efficient mind control and concentration are, as immediate effects at least, quite clearly the strong points of emphasis of the Yogism training. Asked directly whether their power of concentration was improving, only 1 advanced Yoga student in every 100 said that it was not.

Finally, additional psychological improvements that have not been included above were mentioned by the advanced students. One in 6 said his "mind control" and "concentration" had improved, and another 1 in 6 felt "calmer."

Generally, then, the chief psychological benefit that the Yogism students seem to feel is an increased capacity for controlling and calming their mind and emotions. The following examples are more or less typical of this reaction, as well as of others of the psychological rather than the purely physical type:

> I have developed a general steady view of things which, before, would have upset me. Now I get a calm and balanced judgment.

> I am getting more placid, not so irritable, can sit still—a thing I've not been able to do for some time as I had forgotten how to relax—and seem to have lost that tense feeling.

> I used to be short-tempered and on the least thing would snap at my mother (who is bed-ridden) and afterward feel very sorry for it. But now I find myself allowing for her little fads and fancies. Thus we *both* are feeling happier.

> I seem to be filled with a new spirit altogether. Mind-wandering is beginning to vanish and so is worry, slowly but surely. I am more sure of myself in work and play.

> Short temper now controlled and tolerance of others and their onetime irritable habits. Disposition more cheery and less morbid. Self-confidence. Rebirth of religious outlook.

So we come to the conclusions to be drawn from our investigations. Out of every 100 advanced Yogism students whose reports were analyzed:

TABLE 5 *

50 reported greater physical alertness and fitness
18 reported loss of body fat and increased bodily suppleness
30 reported better mental control and powers of concentration
19 reported that they felt calmer

* Percentages exceed 100 even though the table is incomplete because many people mentioned more than one type of improvement.

Greater physical fitness and mental control seem, thus, to be the outstanding immediate benefits of the Yogism training, although examination of the students' reports indicates, as already mentioned, that a great variety of improvements of different kinds, ranging from a better figure to relief from fatigue and a wide assortment of ailments, is also widely experienced.

The following notes will indicate the extent of this enthusiasm:

REPORTED BY BEGINNERS IN YOGISM

Only 1 per cent said that they have found *no* exercises beneficial. The Deep Relaxation and Revitalizing Breath exercises are felt to be particularly helpful.

Chief benefits mentioned were *physical*—relaxation and refreshment, greater physical alertness and fitness and relief of catarrh and clearing of nasal passages.

And on the mental side (less frequent) mostly relaxation and refreshment, sometimes greater alertness and fitness.

REPORTED BY STUDENTS MIDWAY THROUGH THE COURSE

Chief physical benefits were greater alertness and fitness, breathing control and easier breathing, and relief of catarrh and clearing of nasal passages, relief of constipation and indigestion.

Chief *mental* benefits mentioned were better mind control with greater concentration, calmer and more detached outlook—the former mentioned more often than any physical benefit.

REPORTED BY ADVANCED STUDENTS

Chief physical benefits now recounted were greater alertness and fitness, better breathing control, and relaxation.

Chief mental benefits now recounted were mental control and greater powers of concentration.

Exercise most often mentioned as successful was the Yogism breathing technique (by 23 per cent).

Chief physical reason given for exercise proving successful was increased alertness and fitness, absence of excess weight and more supple body, greater physical relaxation.

The chief benefits noted were increased calmness and greater control and concentration.

Eighty-six per cent agreed that their concentration was improving.

Increased mind control and concentration were given as the chief reason for finding the Yogism *lessons* helpful.

As people went on with the Course, they gave more diverse reasons for finding exercises successful or beneficial. Physical relaxation and refreshment were given as the chief initial benefit and, later, greater physical alertness and fitness.

This analysis of 1,000 reports, voluntarily submitted, certainly left us in no doubt that the average student taking the Yogism Course is more than satisfied with the results it produces.

So ends Mass-Observation's analysis and confirmation of the benefits enjoyed by modern Western people who took the Yogism path to healthier, happier living. This report gives clear, independent testimony

1. that a way has been found to apply, in modern times, age-old precepts for a more abundant life;
2. further, that a way has been found whereby the practical West can make use of Eastern mysticism.

Four worlds can thus meet—the ancient with the present-day, the Orient with the West.

We have seen the gaps that civilization leaves in the average person's life. A modern development—public-opinion assessment—has actually enabled us to measure them with some scientific precision. It has also coldly analyzed the happier life experienced by those who have applied the Yogism techniques.

Now, enough of statistics. You, the reader, have, I hope, been convinced by this impressive array of independent testimony that there is something here which deserves looking into. Why be miserable, frustrated, unwell, exhausted if you can be happy, successful, well, and strong? Why, *why?*

Away with skepticism and doubt while you give the Yogism formulas a trial! Reserve your judgment until you, too, can speak from the vantage point of this new sphere of experience.

Read the next chapter and take your first step to your personal freedom. Learn how to free your brain and your body from the greatest scourge of civilized living—the state of high tension. Though not a disease in the accepted sense, it is the first and worst barrier to your long life and happiness.

CHAPTER 3

Step 1 to Liberation: Deep Relaxation

ALREADY every reader of this book is practicing Yogism, albeit in primitive form. But without instruction this instinctive application generally falls short of precision. Hence life remains drab where it could become buoyant. I say this "generally" is the case, but there are certain well-known and fortunate people who have stumbled accidentally on the secret of success; unlike you, they carry their Yogism techniques far enough to experience tangible benefits.

You are already practicing Yogism in part because, basically, it is a simple and natural thing. It merely extends certain well-recognized activities to the stage where they transform ordinary day-to-day living into the full, rounded life. These activities have been identified already as breathing, resting, thinking, and acting. And although *rest* may not be the most important of the four, it is certainly, in this hectic age, the most urgently needed. Its study will also illustrate how Yogism resolves natural functions into their composite details so that a clear technique is obtained for amplifying the good to be obtained from them. In other words, what hitherto has happened willynilly behind the scenes is brought into the open and becomes a full-dress affair. Let us demonstrate.

The greatest curse of civilization is speed. Today a child must know at least ten times more than its grandparents knew at the same age. The vast accumulation of information which the average adult must absorb to carry on his daily work, and conduct intelligent conversation, would have staggered our simple fathers.

Events are now happening a hundred times faster than ever before—by telegraph, telephone, and radio. We are moving a hundred times quicker by road, rail, sea, and air. All the time we are being bombarded by still more new developments, reported *via* radio, telephone, newspapers, ticker tape, and television.

Compare this cacophony with the background enjoyed by your greatgrandfather. He lived quietly near his work. He didn't go by train or bus, fly in the air or travel in the bowels of the earth. He took his time and he always had some part of his day unmolested. The babel of a modern office or factory would have left him thunderstruck. This continuous noise and constant bustle is injurious to health and, in trying to cope with it, nerves can be strained to breaking point.

Modern inventions, so far from giving man more leisure, serve mainly to increase his momentum or activity. There are always more things for him to do; there is always fresh information for him to master. But there is no rest, no respite, no relaxation.

The pay-off for this continuous tension and irritation is seen in recurring outbursts of indigestion, quarrelsomeness, a mounting sense of inferiority, nervous fatigue, etc., etc. If we analyze these phenomena, we will find that the modern tempo of life is a root-cause of each discomfort.

When we lose our tempers, it is usually because we have reached a point beyond which we cannot cope. The cause, in other words, is sheer exhaustion. The feeling of fatigue is likewise due to overstrain. On the go day and night, vainly trying to keep abreast of new excitements, we ask too much of our hard-worked minds and ill-nourished bodies. Some people stay up too late at night and go to bed completely exhausted. They sleep badly and wake unrefreshed. Then they go out and accept more strain—and wonder why they fall ill.

Most illnesses can be traced back to a preceding period of unnatural rush, strain, or tension. One out of every two deaths today over the age of forty-five is due to heart disease. And the type of person most subject to heart disease? He is the high-powered business executive or busy professional man—the type habitually living on his nerves and working all hours.

A quarter of a century ago, duodenal ulcers were a rare complaint. Today they are commonplace. Like colitis—notoriously due to tense, overwrought nerves—this modern illness is a reflection of the common need of relaxation.

Again, the inferiority complex is a by-product of an exhausted, frustrated personality.

And what are *nerves* but the poor, misused body's method of signaling its crying need of rest?

Grasp the fact that every muscular contraction involves a preceding nervous impulse, and you will understand how relaxation may soothe nervous complaints. In relaxation you can shut down the nerve signals. This allows the muscles to stand at ease—otherwise they are either marching about or standing at attention. When relaxed they go limp and, therefore, during any period of enforced relaxation, nervous discharge is diminished, whether you are aware of it or not. Not only the muscles but the nerves themselves enjoy a rest. Yet how much time, during the day, do you now allow for relaxation?

Lord Northcliffe was typical of the type who live completely on their nerves, burning themselves up long before their appointed time. At the age of twenty-three he made a fortune with his newspaper *Answers*—a few years more, and his fertile brain inspired the *Daily Mail;* and then more and still more empires arose to be conquered.

This dazzling genius left behind a trail of stupendous achievement. He worked day and night, collecting fortunes, fame, influence. Today, many years after his death, Fleet Street still throbs with anecdotes of his volcanic activity. Yet Northcliffe might have lived to inspire humanity much longer had he learnt just one lesson—the secret of relaxation.

By a stroke of good fortune Winston Churchill discovered the Relaxation technique—though it was only just in time. In 1915, when he was at the Admiralty, he worried so hard "that my veins threatened to burst. . . . I had great anxiety and no way of relieving it." Painting came to his rescue. Then, as the years went by, he learned to dispense with tension altogether. Painting had pointed the way, and he was quick to learn the moral. In World War II, Churchill bore burdens that would have broken most other men. Indeed, during the years that Churchill captained all the forces of democracy, and faced surely the most grievous personal strains, his personality glowed and thrived. Why? The fact is that when the Churchill batteries ran low, their owner simply recharged them. He lay down and instantly relaxed. It became as simple as changing his overcoat.

Talleyrand was another wise man who acquired this art. When things became troublesome, he always went "into conference." Going "into conference," in his case, meant slipping off to bed. There he lay, no one daring to disturb him. He meditated his problem and then, having considered all the possibilities, he turned on his side and relaxed. He would "awake" refreshed, ready as an eagle for action, and with the solution clear in his head.

Churchill, Northcliffe, and Talleyrand are extreme examples, of course. Compared with their dazzling careers, the average man and woman lead a very insignificant life. Yet we, too, are subject to immense strain, though on a lesser scale. Therefore, no less than the imposing statesman or successful business magnate, we have need of this boon of relaxation.

Relaxing is certainly much pleasanter—and more effective—than throwing fits of temper or plunging into despair when things go against us.

Of course, the idea of relaxation is nothing new. It is an integral part of every therapeutic treatment. Unfortunately, it is seldom understood even by doctors, and involves a good deal more than simply going to bed. In fact, *real relaxation* does not involve going to bed at all. It can be taken in a chair, while traveling by train—best of all, lying on your back on the floor!

Unless (like Mr. Churchill) you develop the gift instinctively, relaxation must be learned by practice. I have devised a routine which can be followed at any time, and especially when you are in most need of rest—for example, during a pause in a trying, anxious or irksome day.

When you are at your wit's end, and everything seems to have turned against you, instead of carrying on the fight with depleted strength, seize the opportunity to relax. Later you will return to action reinvigorated. But it must be *deep* relaxation, not just ordinary relaxation, if you would experience the full boost.

Deep Relaxation means relieving mind and body of all conscious tension and contraction. The very word *relax* gives us a clue to this process. The term is derived from the Latin *laxare,* which means "to loosen or slacken." This original interpretation has much more sense than the modern idea of relaxing by substituting one type of hustle for another. The Deep Relaxation taught in Yogism enables us to "let go" as many muscles as possible and as many thoughts as possible, allowing brain and physique to slump completely—an attitude, if you like, of complete resignation.

This technique is based on an ancient Yogic pose or *asana* known as *Savasan* (Sanskrit for "Death posture"). The Yogis closely studied animal life and based most of their exercises on this observation. They noted that certain animals passed the winter in sleep—a sleep so deep as to have all the appearance of death. Bears, bats, and even the common hedgehog know how to exist for months unfed and unmoving, in this strange, trancelike slumber. Even when not hibernating, all animals can relax at will, certainly far more so than the average human being.

Even the common dog and cat have survived domesticity to the extent of retaining their power of Deep Relaxation. Watch your dog as it moves round in circles preparatory to flopping on the floor. Its body becomes a dead weight, every muscle is placed completely at ease. Yes, your dog is indeed an expert at relaxing and, like all animals, he very sensibly favors the horizontal position—*e.g.,* body in line with

We can learn much about Deep Relaxation from the animal world. This graceful pose, drawn from life, shows a camel relaxed in a way few humans could emulate. Note how the body is slumped in graceful, elegant, satisfying, restful e-a-s-e!

Another true-to-life animal study, showing perfect repose.
It is because we humans have completely forgotten how
to relax that we are continually feeling tired and exhausted. Every human being, just as much as this young
deer, needs the tonic stimulus of true deep relaxation.

This polar tranquility has a lesson for visitors to the Zoo.
We visit the zoo "to relax," but those behind the bars
certainly know a lot more about relaxation than their
tensed, frustrated spectators.

Relaxation in bird life takes characteristic forms. This king penguin (left) acts as though he hadn't a care in the world. And at the time the drawing was made he certainly hadn't, for he was asleep.

Another way of relaxing, though not recommended for humans! This fragile butterfly (right) can remain absolutely motionless—no human being could copy its complete stillness without years of practice.

Silent, unmoving, this wise old adjutant stork takes his rest seriously. Accurately balanced on his hocks, he is not likely to be troubled by the human curse of insomnia.

floor. This is also the best position for human relaxation. A certain amount of muscular contraction (or what physiologists call *tonus*) is needed to keep an upright body from collapsing under its own weight. So, even if you learn my technique for Deep Relaxation, and in due course seek to carry it out in an armchair or while traveling in the train, you will never succeed quite so well as when you practice it in the privacy of your own room and assume the horizontal posture. In the deepest stages of relaxation there is always a residue of muscular contraction. Naturally, this is more pronounced when the muscles have to hold the body upright.

There are some 400 muscles on each side of your body and no fewer than 20 in the forearm alone! Most are beyond your range of conscious feeling. They seem to perform their operations automatically.

Now, if relaxation involves putting your muscles at ease—and, to a large extent, this actually is the case— then we must focus on the principal muscular groups known to us. When you do relax these major muscles, the subsidiary muscles fall into line. To illustrate, let us consider the opposite of relaxation—that is, contraction.

When you lift your arm, you do infinitely more than contract the deltoid muscle. A battalion of ancillary muscles, mostly outside the realm of consciousness, is instantly summoned to action. Tension comes into play, for *all* muscles contract or shorten by an increase of tension (without some tension you would be unable to move). What happens is that a nervous impulse is sent from the brain to the muscles concerned in the moving of your arm. These muscles contract under tension, and so the arm lifts.

In the course of a day you make multitudinous movements of which you are quite unconscious—indeed, during all your waking hours there is a constant drain on your energy through the multiplicity of unnecessary movements which you allow to take place. Most people simply cannot sit still. When not wriggling from side to side, they are throwing their weight from one foot to the other, tapping their fingers, shrugging their shoulders, pursing their lips, wrinkling their brows—just a bundle of *movement*. No wonder we call them "nervous," "high-strung." No wonder they complain of fatigue and exhaustion in the later hours of the day. Really, it is amazing that, after incessant movement all day long, they have any nervous energy left at all in the evening.

Now, none of these reflexes takes place without cause. For just as conscious impulses enable you to raise your arm in order to put on your hat, so impulses of a subconscious nature lie at the back of all the other actions taken by your muscles. You are conscious of muscular contraction when you put out your hand to grasp something. But you may be quite oblivious of the fact that you are tapping your desk impatiently while waiting for a phone call, or clutching the lapels of your jacket when engaged in earnest conversation.

Of course, even deliberate movements, of which you are fully conscious, are accompanied by numerous unknown muscular contractions. Sir Oliver Lodge once remarked to me that if we knew all the actions required in order to walk, we would never stir out of bed.

Every muscle is made up of hundreds of thousands of independent fibres, each with its own nerve telephone. And so for every physical movement, not just one muscle, with its 100,000 nerve connections, but whole groups of muscles, each with their 100,000 telephones, are summoned to Action Stations! Even to move your little finger involves a remarkable output of nervous intelligence and energy. You may be conscious only of the *will* to move your finger, but a whole systemized operation, as complicated as moving a military division in the field, has to be broken down, organized and schemed in the subconscious theater of your mind.

Consider, then, the multifarious activity of this kind that goes into the making of a single day; or the extra strain imposed when you hustle through things at top speed. What a colossal expenditure of planning and energy! Is it any wonder you are often exhausted, completely played out, by evening? Sheer fatigue can make you quite miserable; and *your* misery, you know, can soon put others in bad humor.

Now look at this thing another way. First, a question. Can you doubt that the curtailment of unnecessary nervous discharge would help you reduce the strain, and make the long day happier? Of course not. This business of relaxation is common sense. Of course, one needn't bother about relaxing all the hundreds of thousands of muscular nerve ends. Nor even about the many muscles which one can't feel. All you need think about are the prominent skeletal muscles—those you do feel acting when making a voluntary movement. Learn to relax these major muscle groups, and the others will automatically respond likewise.

The very first step, then, to Deep Relaxation is *to cultivate the desire to enjoy it.* That created, you are halfway to satisfaction. Which is why I have been engaged in stimulating your interest in this technique for Deep Relaxation and, I hope, instilling within you the wish to experiment with it. Enough should already have been said to convince you of the need to relax frequently. Now we can deal with how to relax. Some readers will find this easier than others. The high-strung type will find it hardest of all, and, perversely, they have most need of it. But even those who find it hard at first can master it in time, given sufficient perseverance. They should remember, as they make their first half-successful attempts, that any depth of quiet relaxation is better than none at all. Even a poor relaxation period will bestow a certain amount of rest. Skill, which brings depth, grows with practice, as in all arts.

Study these first rules: (1) You must want to relax. (2) You must realize it is not a newfangled craze but an age-old and obviously sensible practice. (3) You must decide to practice it at regular intervals. And (4) you must understand that *Deep* Relaxation cannot be forced. In other words, don't make the mistake of trying too hard, for that simply stops you from relaxing at all. Gently, smoothly, patiently, must be your line of approach. If you try too hard or become impatient, you will set up a feeling of tension. Tension involves muscular contraction—the very thing which we are striving to avoid.

Choose a place and a time when you are sure to be undisturbed. *This is vital*. You are making the attempt to shut out all sensation. If someone bursts suddenly into the room, you'll be brought back from your reverie abruptly and unpleasantly. Therefore, the place for Deep Relaxation should be as quiet as practicable. (The noise of traffic, incidentally, is less disturbing than the rhythmic sound of machinery or the regular beat of a clock.)

Having decided upon the room, you must next decide what position you will adopt when seeking relaxation. The best position is on the floor. A bed is too soft and yielding; you may fall asleep. Although that would be better than nothing, the type of Deep Relaxation taught by Yogism is not intended to take the place of sleep but to supplement it. The two are quite different states, and each has its own distinctive quality.

Ordinary sleep doesn't completely rest the body half as much as imagined. A half-hour's nap after lunch or dinner is a good habit, but ten minutes' Deep Relaxation is better. People can be confined to bed for years, nodding from time to time during the day and night, and yet feel genuinely exhausted and tired. If you imagine ordinary sleep is tension-free, think again. During eight hours' sleep, the average period free from movement is about twelve minutes —for many people, even less. During sleep you are all the time contracting muscles, shifting and changing your position, to say nothing of the mental unrest caused by dreams. Deep Relaxation is quite different from sleep because, among other things, it rules out all muscular contraction.

So, if convenient, choose the floor, not the bed, for Deep Relaxation. This means putting down a rug to lie upon, and perhaps another rug to trap possible drafts. Obviously, the room must be made draft-free and warm if you are going to lie on the floor and rest. I am afraid these are minimum requirements for your first experiments. Later you need not be so fastidious about your surroundings. But to get a fair depth of relaxation quickly you must be free from cold, drafts, noise, and disturbance.

We will suppose you are now lying on your back on the floor—perhaps the floorboards feel hard, but that is better than a soft bed. Don't make the mistake of shifting every now and then to find a more easy position; having assumed a comfortable posture, with your weight fairly distributed, hold it. Movement should be checked—any change of position, however slight, will upset what follows. Just try to distribute your weight evenly on the floor and resolve, come what may, to leave your weight and posture there, undisturbed.

Now stretch an arm, leg, or even your neck or feet —any part of the body. Stretch it hard, make the muscles contract, *and study what is happening.* (You'll be surprised at the way in which parts far removed from the seat of operations contract in sympathy. A strongly clenched fist, for example, will cause contractions to be felt all the way up your arm and down your shoulders and back.) Hold the stretch while you trace these sensations in detail, then let go. This completes Step 1.

Now, for your next step toward Deep Relaxation, stretch hard again—but this time, do it in slow motion. Build the stretch up slowly and observe and note every sensation inspired by it. Again, hold the stretch while you make a mental record of all that is happening. Then, once more in slow motion, let go. Here, now, is the secret of success; you must let go as slowly as possible, *carrying the "let-go" process beyond the point where you have ceased to be conscious of any physical sensation whatsoever.* Continue further with this "let-go" mechanism until you reach the stage where you are no longer *trying* to relax but have completely lost all feeling of alertness in the portions of your anatomy concerned.

It will be enough for your first attempts to direct your attention to one part of the body only. With repetition, your application of these principles should become more general, until you cease to think of specific areas and commence relaxing the whole body as a coordinated unit. From time to time, as you relax, you will become aware of muscle groups that have escaped attention or, having been relaxed at first, have again grown tense; they must be newly relaxed, of course. But remember not to make too much of an effort in your first attempts. Remember, too, that *any* success is worth accepting, however small—*any* relaxation is more beneficial than none.

I have found that students who begin by being concerned about what they can't do invariably take longer to succeed with what they *can*. Therefore, don't be too hard on yourself or too impatient or too exacting when you begin. Be content with partial success. You will deepen your relaxation progressively, as you continue the daily practice.

After a time you will develop a definite sequence for Deep Relaxation—you will stop darting attention from this to that group of muscles. You will discover that it is best to begin with the head and then pass down the body, relaxing groups of muscles as you find them, easing the arms from the shoulders, the legs from the hips, and so on. But when you have completed this mental review and diminished the feeling of tension and alertness right down to the toes, you must turn back to the eyebrows, eyelids, and eyeballs. For these are the hardest parts of your anatomy to relax—this region which is, by proximity, most closely related to the organ of sight. There is almost sure to be some contraction here which normally escapes notice and needs relaxing a second or third time.

This, then, is the technique for Deep Relaxation, so far as it can be given in a book. But you have been given sufficient material to start working, and the results should encourage you to keep the practice up. The question arises: How often, and for how long, should these Deep Relaxation periods be conducted? Never let them be for less than five minutes; there is no maximum time. If you can afford fifteen minutes or even half an hour, you won't find it too long. In fact, benefits accrue, in the early stages, in proportion to the amount of time you give to relaxation. Later, there will be as much response from a lesser period of increased *depth*.

How often? Ideally, at the start of the day, if you can manage it. There is nothing like Deep Relaxation to set the tone, so to speak, to a quiet, well-controlled, happy, and successful day. Similarly, it is unsurpassed as a preliminary to any special endeavor—before setting forth to an important meeting, for example, or prior to engaging in any trial of strength.

Deep Relaxation should also be practiced in the evening, on coming home from work. Nothing so quickly spoils your few leisure hours as nervous fatigue. Sweep it away, then, by a short period of Deep Relaxation, during which the effect of the day's irritations, tensions, and emotions can be calmed down, drained off, and replaced by an invigorated, refreshed condition of mind.

Many people feel more in need of a "lift" at midday. They usually seek it in a glass, and then feel drowsy all afternoon. Deep Relaxation would give them all the "kick" they need. Their minds would become far clearer and more alert, their work more efficient, than could be achieved by any artificial stimulant.

Give Deep Relaxation a place in your life every day for a week, and you will never revert to the old fixed ways. You'll start storing up energy as well as running it down. Indeed, without a daily period of Deep Relaxation, it is impossible for your body or mind to approach anything like 100-per-cent fitness. Remember, when you are *not* relaxing you are tense. And tension drains energy. *High* tension, which arises when you are excited, worked up, or frustrated, drains energy faster still.

Again, when you have any really big trouble, don't panic. It will look better—and clearer—after a period of Deep Relaxation. Lie down and relax the way you have now been taught. If this is out of the question, sit in a comfortable chair, and go through the motions of relaxing from head to foot. You'll soon eliminate the feeling of suspense and pressure, and then you will be able to do a better job. You will have stopped tension at its source.

Women should note that tension and aging are synonymous. It is tension that adds wrinkles to the brow, gives a stoop to the shoulder. And there is nothing like it for putting lead into your heart. If you want to grow old before your time, don't relax. Keep on the move. Get haggard and old, wear yourself out. In other words, don't relax!

As it happens, a very active career can be followed if there are regular periods of Deep Relaxation to rebuild the energy expended in living at high pressure. If you are a man and your ambition is to employ a large staff and carry heavy responsibility, you have little prospect of long life and happiness unless you make good the "run-down" in nervous strength by relaxing—the deeper, the better. Unless you do this, you are booking a future bed in the hospital.

Of course, you may be lucky enough to work in a business which gradually demands less of you. Then the pressure is run down, not you. But most business executives are expected to keep on performing miracles. Yesterday's records are the targets to be broken tomorrow. Naturally, these circumstances precipitate breakdowns, not only of men but of methods.

As he moves idly through the water, this pike is a picture of graceful, effortless motion—a fine example of how to relax, even in action.

This chimpanzee seems to prefer the human idea of relaxation—huddled up tight with muscles contracted rather than at ease. A very good example of how NOT to do it! Is it only coincidence that a beast so closely related to the human family should relax so indifferently?

Female seal with young on the Antarctic ice. Animals are always to be seen in their most relaxed state when resting with their young. It may be one of nature's methods of handing on the secret.

Half the troubles of this world are due to the actions and decisions of tensed-up, exhausted men sitting in places of authority. They are tired men, carrying too heavy a load, and they just can't see straight or act clearly. People who need a rest can't make wise decisions. Heaven only knows how many world wars would have been avoided if statesmen had only known this secret of Deep Relaxation!

Living one's life as though the next moment were the last is the surest way of abbreviating it. To the ancient Yogis, there was no such thing as death. They looked beyond death to a new world of opportunity. Believing this wholeheartedly, they saw no point in rushing and getting flustered; they relaxed because eternity lay before them. The value they attached to relaxation, therefore, arose in the first instance from a deeply mystical attitude to life. It is an attitude which has the sanction of Christian experience. In fact, all the great religions were pioneered by leaders who practiced relaxation in one form or another. Invariably there was a period of withdrawal from worldly scenes. When Jesus went into the wilderness, He practiced relaxation. When He said "The Kingdom of Heaven is within," He meant us to enter that Kingdom if we would know His peace.

Deep Relaxation has also the authority of history. A subconscious awareness that there is something specially significant about Drake's famous game of bowls has possessed every English schoolchild for decades. I believe it arises from the instinctive feeling that Drake was right in relaxing in face of mortal peril—that a brief spell spent in quiet before the supreme ordeal would serve him better than wasting his energies in warlike agitation.

Much has been said about tension, but it must be realized that tension of itself is not an evil thing; it is *high* tension that does the damage. Without tension of some kind we could not flex the muscles at all. What is wrong is unnecessary, destructive tension.

Boxers fail to land the crucial punch not from lack of energy or skill but because they are too tense. Spectators at a World Series game have again and again seen the championship flag wrested from a brilliant team because the players were too tense. (The atmosphere on the ball field positively reeks of high tension.) The golfer dubs his shot not because he has misjudged his lie but because he is too tense. The clever student can know the correct answers to an examination paper but fail to record them because he is too tense. The candidate for a coveted job wrecks his chances at the all-important interview because he is too tense. The aspiring pianist makes mistakes at the big concert because he is too tense.

But—the maestro, the champion, the master of every art and craft, excels because he can relax. See him in action: those muscles not wanted for major operations are "laid off" temporarily. He is not running all over with discharging nervous energy, flustered, hot-headed, short-breathed, scared. He gives an impression of elegance and ease—the whole performance looks simple and effortless.

If, then, you crave success in any field of endeavor —in art, athletics, salesmanship, golf, scholarship, it matters not—recognize high tension as your enemy,

Deep Relaxation as your friend. Recall what happened when you first learned to drive a car; how tensely you gripped the steering wheel, how tensely you peered at the road ahead, how tensely you felt the nerves of your foot as you tried to operate the clutch ... and what a mess you made of it! But once you learned to steer, peer, and change gear when relaxed, you drove smoothly, efficiently, and safely.

So with life. Don't grip *that* steering wheel with such grim, ruthless determination. Learn Deep Relaxation! And when you have learned to relax fully, so that you can turn off tension at will, give your attention to other applications of this principle. Apply it to all the little things. Relax instead of frittering away your energies in unproductive movements; that swinging foot, when you sit with your legs crossed; the habit of shifting about in your chair as though it were electrically charged—get wise to these unproductive movements and stop the drain. Need you grip your pipe quite so violently? Must you hold your pen with such venom? Need you shout down the telephone? Or snap at those who don't immediately agree with you?

The principle of relaxation can be carried into everyday life in all sorts of ways to lighten the load and ease the strain. But Deep Relaxation has a deeper purpose than has yet been hinted.

There is something more to this technique than merely letting go of nervous tension, recharging your run-down battery, and cutting short unnecessary movement. My investigations show that a daily Deep Relaxation session cultivates a more detached outlook at all times. This attitude of detachment can have the most far-reaching implications for your long life and happiness. For you cease then to identify yourself so closely with what is happening in the world about you. You grow more independent. Your face begins to look younger; your habits and gestures become more economical. Your sleep becomes sounder.

After a period of Deep Relaxation take a look at your face. You will see proof that it has lost some of the old worried look. The healing and rejuvenating properties are there on show. Friends will comment on your younger, brighter appearance as your skill in Deep Relaxation grows. You will enjoy longer life because you will be *putting back as well as taking*. And since you'll know how to stand back from life and not exhaust yourself in the fray, your increased happiness goes without saying.

My technique of Deep Relaxation, although based on the Yogic death pose, involves much more than rest as normally understood. It has something in common with the reverie of the painter. It has something in common with the monk's "sweet hour of prayer." It has something in common with the ecstasy of the mystic. But it is not any of these things singly. Nor does it purport to reproduce their varied phenomena.

Deep Relaxation is an altogether more deliberate, practical, and everyday affair. Because it can be undertaken consciously, it can be practiced by all. And its chief virtue is the renewing of the self within.

CHAPTER 4

Step 2 to Liberation: Deep Contraction

AFTER Deep Relaxation, Deep Contraction! Yes, that is the order if you would follow this program for long life and happiness. To begin with, look at the accompanying pictures of animals engaged in simple, instinctive stretching movements that give an insight into Deep Contraction.

I suggest that you should not only glance at these pictures but study each with some care. More than any words, they describe the smooth, rhythmical sustained, and graceful movements that are part of everyday animal life of the subhuman order. These "lower" animals have, indeed, much they could teach us.

Come to think of it, what a miserable lot of specimens the average railway coach contains! Compared with an equal number of animals of any other breed, the human beings will be an ill-assorted lot. Some have sagging abdomens, some stooping shoulders, some flat chests—it is extraordinary how many malformations can be developed by the human form. The dog world, could it organize a human show

comparable to our dog shows, would be appalled at
the variety of the entrants!

The infinite variations, embellishments, and deg-
radations of the human form arise from man's
unique freedom of will. He can elect to live a natural
life or he can choose an artificial one. Certain circumstances conspire to influence his decision, of
course, but basically he is a free agent—certainly
much freer than the lower animals. Having received
this power to choose, he can, naturally, exercise it
unwisely. Hence the distended stomachs, sallow
cheeks, and all the rest of the "points" which would
make judging a human show something of a canine
nightmare.

As for the bodies which would be on display, the
exercise they are given is generally of the most
checkered kind. Mainly it is confined to getting up,
dressing, talking, walking, sitting, eating, and going
to bed. The odd round of golf, occasional game of
cards, or unpleasant climb upstairs (when the elevator
is out of order) are the main "relaxations" of the
average civilized man. And yet the most discouraging
thing to anyone convinced of the need of exercise is
the standard textbook on physical culture. It advocates dull routines of the most unimaginative type. To
obtain results, these exercises need to be performed
an infinite number of times. The whole thing smacks
of too much effort and strain for the not-quite-so-fit,
and they soon learn to leave it alone.

Now, I claim that the most pleasant and stimulating
of all physical exercises are natural, spontaneous body
movements. Good examples are the yawn (a passive

form of muscular contraction) and the running jump to clear a small obstacle (an active form of muscular contraction). There is a sense of satisfaction about these simple movements which all artificial exercises entirely lack. No hunter has ever seen a lion, a bear, or, indeed, any creature renowned for its strength engaged in repetitions of knee bends and similar exercises.

This does not mean that physical culture, as practiced in the West, has no place. It is unbeatable for improving track records, building bodily bulk, and increasing physical agility. Yet even here, in its own sphere, it can learn from Yogism.

Ever seen a horse at play? He springs into action, flushed with the joy of life—and shows the cleansing, reviving, stimulating "tonic" of natural muscle tension.

No, this cormorant isn't preparing to fly. Many times you have seen birds flapping their wings, yet with no intention of flight. They are simply keeping their bodies young, strong, and fit by obeying nature's impulse.

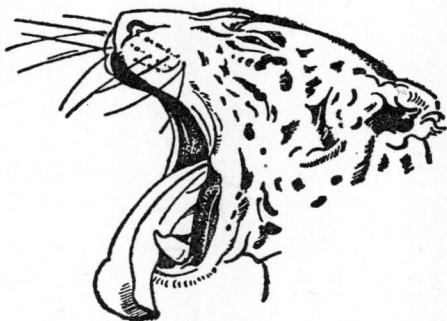

It may not be good manners to yawn in public, but no such petty convention impedes the jaguar. Emulate this yawn—when nobody is looking! You will be astonished at the bracing effect on muscles in the throat, chest, back, abdomen, forehead, and face. Even your shoulders will share the invigorating tonic. But you must yawn really deeply—and prolong the yawn—to enjoy the full effects.

Let Reginald Park, our leading authority on Western physical culture, give his testimony. Mr. Park can speak confidently, having created a physique which, in open competition, has won him the titles, "Mr. Universe," "Mr. Britain" and "Mr. Europe," and other peak physical culture laurels:

I have studied the Yogism course [he writes me] and I feel it will be a wonderful help to many on the lookout for something to help them improve. It will give them the incentive they need. It will help them to derive the utmost benefit by creating a healthy mind and body. I am sure Yogism will prove a boon and a blessing.

A generous acknowledgment, this, from one who has so successfully practiced the Western way of physical development. It is echoed by other well-known athletes who have studied Yogism.

Jock McAvoy was the greatest boxer of his time. He was middleweight champion of Great Britain and the British Empire for eleven years, retiring undefeated. He won the Lonsdale Belt outright and was light heavyweight champion of Great Britain and the British Empire. A man with such a record should know something of physical excellence. He writes:

I have studied Yogism and consider it of great benefit. In my opinion, it is absolutely invaluable to anyone engaged in athletic pursuits of any kind, but especially in boxing. I have myself derived great benefits from the Course and put inches on my chest and felt much better generally. I think this Yogism should be taken by everybody, including amateur and professional boxers, and I wish it great success.

Laurie Buxton, chairman of the Professional Boxers' Association and a leading lightweight contender, is another athlete who has adopted the Yogism exercises. He writes:

Yogism has shown me an entirely new approach to the problem of training and has enabled me to give my utmost with the minimum of physical strain. The beauty of Yogism is that it can be applied by women and men of all ages—anyone who seeks true mental or physical fitness can take it up as far as he likes and gain real improvement.

In this last sentence, Mr. Buxton has touched the unique fact about these exercises. Not everyone aspires to be a world-beater, in or out of the ring, and it would be entirely wrong to imagine that Yogism was intended only for athletic aspirants. While it works for the young and fit, thereby enabling them to obtain their maximum physical development, it is equally serviceable for the middle-aged and elderly. Moreover, it can be readily applied by both sexes. These features are unique. Remember, some parts of the body are hardly ever exercised in normal physical activities. The deposits formed result in the muscles, tendons, and nerves becoming "set" and sluggish—a condition which often leads to rheumatism and other painful ailments. Even when these maladies do not appear, natural elasticity is greatly reduced by failure to exercise the unused parts of the body. But, during Deep Contraction, all muscle groups are loosened, deposits are broken down, waste is washed away, and the whole physique is made trim and healthy.

Of course, there is a limit beyond which no transformation can be performed. In slimming by Yogism or other exercises, it is impossible to reduce the hips more than the width allowed by the pelvis. Every bodily framework has certain maximum and minimum possibilities which just cannot be exceeded. If you are the square-built type, you cannot change overnight to the tall, elongated type. There is certainly a limit to height, even if, touching forty, you are beginning to suspect no limit to girth!

Within certain confines it *is* possible—nay, easy— to make the best or the worst of one's prospects. You can work off fat, improve your carriage, put zip into your step, bring color into your cheeks, and inspire vivacity into life generally. You can acquire greater or lesser bodily bulk according to your needs. The Deep Contraction technique will see to this automatically because there is a "natural" figure for you—a figure which will show you at your best and most attractive —and this is what you develop when leading the Yogism life. To develop it may involve some planning and work, yet neither need be strenuous. Heavy physical exercise is all very well for the young and fit. It is not such a good thing for the less young and not so fit. And since all young people must one day grow old, I will ask their forbearance while I now deal specifically with the problem of the neglected middle-aged.

The first thing to be grasped is that this so-called "middle age" does not necessarily signal diminishing health and vitality. Unfortunately, this is exactly what it does mean in most cases, from the age of forty upward. But it need not! It is not inevitable and it is certainly not natural to "go to pieces" at fifty.

That the aging process usually begins to manifest so soon is due entirely to man's own folly. Animals live five times their maturity; men and women only twice or three times theirs. Why? Wild animals keep their full vigor and appearance for five sixths of their life—but humans begin to lose their vitality and appearance when only three sixths of their life is gone. Why? *Why?*

In his forties and fifties, a man has tasted most of the "sweet things" of civilized life. He has gained that modicum of power which it is necessary to have in order to indulge his fancies. He surrounds himself with creature comforts which were unavailable (and, also, unwanted) in lusty youth. He enjoys the pleasures of the table and begins to study his "convenience." In the ordinary run of things, promotion in his work, which often comes with seniority, brings a curtailment of his youthful physical activity. Now he tells others what to do—his "work" is to give the orders. Where formerly he was content to walk, now the increased value of his time (no less than his own concern for an easy passage) will encourage him to ride. Give him the alternative of walking or riding, and he will invariably choose the soft seat of a car.

Through overeating he is probably already suffering from constipation. Through inaction, increasing rigidity of the spinal column has diminished his body's elasticity. He "stiffens up" and Age puts its heavy hand on his shoulder. He begins to *feel* older as his joints lose their early flexibility. Other signs of aging are to be found in the furrowed forehead and stooping gait, the fading hair, and that haggard look which now steals across his face when fatigued or facing strain. Above all, there develops a well-advertised "middle-aged spread."

Now a vicious circle of events comes into operation. Increasing rotundity will encourage him to limit movement. No wonder surplus fat forms round the posterior and abdomen—both parts of the anatomy which are allowed to sag in the misleading comfort of easy chairs. Not only increasing girth but increasing weight encourage the middle-aged to cut down bending, stooping, and other "unnecessary" movements. Thus, the healthy, natural springtime of life, the period when men and women have reached their prime (and should therefore be enjoying life) becomes unhealthy "middle age"—and the poor ill-cared-for body rolls steadily downhill.

Deep Contraction will help stop this merciless process. The sooner begun, the easier. It is based on ancient Yogic *asanas* or postures. According to tradition, the number of *asanas* is 84 times 100,000! With such an elaborate repertoire, some selection must clearly be made. In fact, the *asanas* were long ago reduced to 84 basic movements. Even so, further pruning was necessary for my system. Few Western people would have the time to do 84 physical convolutions before dressing for breakfast! They need not despair. For the purpose of this book it is unnecessary to learn any set exercise. First grasp the principle of Deep Contraction, before you bother to learn any particular routine. All Deep Contraction is simply the prolongation of a natural, instinctive stretch to the stage where one's whole mood and physique become involved in it. The traditional Yogic *asanas* call for a certain amount of agility. Many are impossible to master unless learned early in life, while the body is still very supple. Even so, I have succeeded in breaking down several of the most important *asanas* into easy stages so that they can be acquired progressively by middle-aged people.

However, to begin with, the Western student should confine himself to simple, natural, *impromptu* stretches of his own devising carried out while (1) sitting down, (2) while lying on the back, and (3) when in the upright or standing posture. Henceforth, every day, stretch in each of these postures in turn *and give at least five minutes to the process.* Encourage your body to stretch slowly this way and that, holding each stretch for a minute or more if possible. Stretch your neck, chest, arms, back, and waist—let the movements be natural, smooth, and, above all, prolonged. During each stretch try to contract as many muscles as you can trace. Beware of sudden jerky movements —stretch slowly, gradually building-up and, equally gradually, playing down the amount of energy and muscular tension involved.

In particular, pay special attention to the waist and back. These are the areas of the abdominal organs and the spine. Much more so than arms and limbs, they have the power to bring long life and happiness. In the abdominal region are situated the internal organs concerned with digestion and elimination. The spinal column—that great trunk line of the nervous system, with connections to every extremity of the body—also directly influences longevity and health.

In case you want further prompting on the exact form of the Deep Contractions, let us assume you have just finished a period of Deep Relaxation—the opposite state, in which all your body has been "at ease." You are lying on the floor, your feet outstretched, arms by sides, face upward.* The Relaxation period has ended. Now, try lifting your left and right legs from the ground level. Do it very *slowly,* holding the legs stiff and pointing them straight out in line with the body. Immediately you will become conscious of a variety of contractions extending from the feet, up the calf, to the thighs, and still on upward to the abdominal region. Hold this stretch as long as possible; then *gently and slowly* lower the feet to the floor, in one smooth, controlled movement —and rest! Though you will not know it, you will have completed the first step to the mastery of two potent Yogic *asanas*—"Sarvangasana" and "Halasana." †

Now, sitting up on the floor, try to grasp your toes or ankles with your left and right hands, bending down the trunk and keeping the legs well outstretched. Continue to bend as deeply as possible and hold the position for some time before gradually loosening your grip and returning, *slowly,* to the upright position.

Again you have indulged a natural stretch—but

* See page 148—Mrtasana (or Savasana).
† See page 152.

you have also taken the first step to another advanced
Yogic exercise—"Pascimottanasana," noted for its
value in energizing the abdomen and spine.

Next lie in the horizontal position, this time with
the face to the floor. Keep your legs straight out behind you and rest the hands on the floor in a line
with the shoulders. Try now to elevate the body by
pressing down on the hands. After some regular daily
practice you will be able to lift the abdomen off the
floor. And you will have performed part of the *asana*
known as "Bhujangasan"—yet another famous stretch
for the spine.

Finally, stretch in the standing position. This you
might do by placing the hands on the thighs and,
after expelling the breath, attempt to lift the abdomen, holding it up. This, again, is part of an ancient
Yogic *asana*. It is actually the first step to "Uddiyana
Bandha."

The foregoing stretching routines are suggestions
only. Follow them if you wish—but also try stretches
of your own devising. I repeat, *any* natural body
stretch can be performed at this stage with immediate
benefit, providing you stretch *slowly—deliberately* . . .
dynamically, and hold it for as long as you can without straining. Spend five minutes or so on these
Contraction exercises every morning, *after* your Deep
Relaxation period. Or do them in the evening, if that
is more convenient. Either period has its advantage.
In the morning you will carry out your Deep Contractions while the stomach is empty, which is the
ideal state; in the evening your muscles will be more
responsive and you should be able to increase the

intensity of each contraction. Any time is suitable providing two or three hours have elapsed since taking food.

During the performance of these Deep Contractions your mental attitude is of importance. Don't make the mistake of performing them in the fashion of a physical-culture exercise. Spend some time on each stretch, study its action, and pause to relish and enjoy it. Be ready to feel the good it is doing you, there and then—there will be no doubt in your mind afterward.

I could fill many pages with diagrams and descriptions of intricate Yogic *asanas,* but I purposely refrain. Even in my own postal instruction, I do not allow students to attempt the traditional *asanas* until they have undergone a month or more of natural, instinctive, "home-made" stretches of their own devising. Much harm occurs when Westerners attempt complicated Yogic postures without this essential preliminary warming-up. Moreover, the *asanas* can best be learned in a step-by-step fashion, and this carefully graduated personal instruction is impossible to undertake in book form.

No reader should neglect the foregoing hints on account of their apparent simplicity. The acid test is *trial.* Spend at least five minutes daily in Deep Contractions of the type described and in seven days you will feel greater elasticity and a new physical and mental exhilaration. Why? Because you have stimulated the spine, lungs, nerves, and internal organs in a way they can never be stimulated by normal movement or physical "jerks."

The difference between Deep Contraction and ordinary physical culture should now be apparent. Whereas the latter makes a fetish of body bulk, big arms, bulging legs, massive chests, and so on, Yogism does not seek to build massive dimensions. For those who seek mere bulk and girth, Western physical culture has no peer. Unfortunately, it stops there, paying little attention to the equally important mental development and need for coordination between mind and body. Its fatiguing nature renders it unattractive to the tired "middle-aged" man or woman desirous of regaining his lost vitality. Weight-lifting and similar Western methods, ideal for young men in the full flood of exuberant youth, have little to offer the beginner over forty. Moreover, some types of Western physical culture, good as they are, exert strong pressure on the heart and arterial system and are positively dangerous to the ailing or elderly. The strain imposed explains why so many athletes are short-lived.

My system of Deep Contraction is not concerned with "developing" individual parts of the body. I focus attention on the *whole* man. Yogism creates a balanced mental–physical combination, not simply muscular strength. It aims at stamina, staying-power, vitality, and sound nerves. And, paradoxically, in so far as it glorifies any specific parts of the body at all, the regions highlighted differ from those featured in ordinary physical training. In Deep Contraction it is the muscle groups and skin areas which are not normally exercised that are most galvanized into action. First, the skin is stretched and pulled this way and that. The whole epidermis is given a tonic

blood-flush. This is very important. In a piece of skin
the size of a postage stamp there are some 3,000,000
cells, a yard of blood vessels, 4 yards of nerves, 100
sweat glands, 15 oil glands, and 25 nerve endings!
These figures indicate the complexity of a physical
organism usually taken for granted. So when you
engage in a skin stretch, a vast and complicated part
of your system is nourished.

When the *muscles* are stretched during Deep Contraction, a lubricant known as synovial fluid is
secreted, and this helps disperse deposits congregating
at the joints. Lymph, a substance made up of plasma,
is stimulated, and the cells of the body which feed on
it are thus actively fortified. Waste products are
washed away by the cleansing blood flush, to be dis-

Now, in the first delicious moments of waking, she rolls
over onto her back, stretching one flipper pleasurably
into the air—just as you yourself do in the early morning
in bed!

Watch the movements of your cat at play, as here. Better still, note how he behaves when he has finished relaxing. The outstretched paws, extended hind feet, and arched back of the waking cat show natural contraction at work.

The "big cats," too, know all about Deep Contraction. Stretching, for a tiger, is a full-dress affair. It is done slowly, the stretch is prolonged, and every muscle group is given a really good, stimulating blood flush.

posed of through the various eliminatory organs. (More of this, later, when we consider the next step.)

Again, during Deep Contraction there is a physical and mental inter-action. The stretching is not done jerkily or haphazardly—all one's attention is concentrated on the development, build-up, and maintenance of the stretch concerned. It is quite impossible to practice Deep Contraction while thinking of something else.

Not to be overlooked are the biochemical changes resulting from Deep Contraction. A whole chemical system is set in motion when groups of muscles are dynamically engaged in a prolonged stretch. The resulting secretions and burning-up processes revive and cleanse all internal parts of the body.

Like Deep Relaxation, Deep Contraction is the extension of a fundamental process normally given scant attention. Basically, Deep Contraction is movement, but movement of a special kind—movement that takes place under dynamic and controlled conditions. During this movement, while some muscles are stimulated strongly, others are allowed to completely rest—thus extending to these remoter areas the good effects of Relaxation. This interweaving of Yogism techniques is most striking in the case of the more deep-seated internal organs which, during Deep Contraction, are either activated or relaxed in a way which could not otherwise be achieved.

Not only is Deep Contraction ideally suited for those who are getting on in years—a child of eight can apply it. Naturally, children will achieve quicker physical exhilaration than their elders because of the unspoiled elasticity of their bodies. On the other hand, they perform the stretches unimaginatively and fail to get the associated mental stimulus.

Finally, Deep Contraction is suitable for all who recoil from violent exercises for fear of developing hefty muscles. Slimming is more naturally achieved by Yogism than by special (and often harmful) diets, drugs, injections, and medicines. By stimulating the abdominal organs, Deep Contraction deals directly with the fat-accumulating areas.

Yet for all the importance attached to it, Deep Contraction is one element only in the four-way plan for living longer and more happily. All this time we have been studying Deep Relaxation and Contraction, we have, of course, been breathing. As will be seen from the next chapter, this most automatic of normal functions can also be adapted to encourage better living. It is the third step to self-mastery.

CHAPTER 5

Step 3 to Liberation: Dynamic Breathing

MY SYSTEM of Dynamic Breathing is based on early Yogic researches into what was then known as the "science of breath." For thousands of years Hindu psychologists have studied breath. They examined it from the practical, physiological, and mystical point of view. To them breathing was more, much more, than just a necessary element of life.

While the body can be sustained for long periods without sleep or food, it cannot live more than a few moments without breath. The Yogis thought this fact not without significance. Just how large a part breath played in early Indian philosophy may be gauged from the following charming tale, culled from one of the oldest scriptures in the world—the *Brihadaranyaka Upanishad:*

The senses, when quarreling together as to who was the best, went to Brahma and said: "Who is the richest of us?" He replied: "He by whose departure the body seems worst, he is the richest."

The tongue (speech) departed, and having been absent for a year, it came back and said: "How have you been able to live without me?" They replied: "Like unto people, not speaking with the tongue, but breathing with the breath, seeing with the eye, hearing with the ear, knowing with the mind, generating with the seed. Thus we have lived." Then speech returned to its place.

The eye (sight) departed, and having been absent for a year, it came back and said: "How have you been able to live without me?" They replied: "Like blind people, not seeing with the eye, but breathing with the breath, speaking with the tongue, hearing with the ear, knowing with the mind, generating with the seed. Thus we have lived." Then the eye returned to its place.

The ear (hearing) departed, and having been absent for a year, it came back and said: "How have you been able to live without me?" They replied: "Like deaf people, not hearing with the ear, but breathing with the breath, speaking with the tongue, seeing with the eye, knowing with the mind, generating with the seed. Thus we have lived." Then the ear returned to its place.

The mind departed, and having been absent for a year, it came back and said: "How have you been able to live without me?" They replied: "Like fools, not knowing with the mind, but breathing with the breath, seeing with the eye, hearing with the ear, speaking with the tongue, generating with the seed. Thus we have lived." Then the mind returned to its place.

The seed departed, and having been absent for a year, it came back and said: "How have you been able to live without me?" They replied: "Like impotent people, not generating with seed, but breathing with the breath, seeing with the eye, hearing with the ear, speaking with

the tongue, knowing with the mind. Thus we have lived."
Then the seed returned to its place.

Now it was the turn of the breath. And on the point of
departing, it tore up the other senses—as a great, excellent horse of the Sindhu country might tear up the pegs
to which he was tethered. Then all the other senses called
out to him, "Sir, do not depart. We shall not be able to
live without thee!"

This legend illustrates the mystical attitude in
which the Yogis approached the subject of respiration.
Were they wrong in giving it such an exalted place?
We practical moderns must admit that of all the life
lines on which we rely, on none are we so absolutely
dependent as on the act of breathing. In a single day
you breathe something like 23,000 times. So great
was the control which the Yogis achieved over respiration that they were able to suspend breathing for an
indefinite period. There are many authenticated in-
stances of Indian *swamis* being "buried alive," without air, to re-emerge, days later, none the worse for
the experience. Here is just one typical case—reported
by the United Press from Bombay. The Yogi was
buried alive for eighty-seven hours, without any ill
effect:

Huge crowds which gathered here from early this
morning saw the 45-year-old Yogi, Swami Randasji, dug
out alive from an airtight cement crypt in which he had
been "buried" for eighty-seven hours.

To make things even tougher, the little man with the
big black beard has been completely submerged in water
since four o'clock on Saturday afternoon until his release

at half-past seven o'clock this morning, after spending three and a half days in the coffinlike niche.

Swami climbed into the wooden coffin at five o'clock last Wednesday afternoon. The coffin was then sealed inside a cement crypt measuring eight feet by six feet. On top of the crypt his followers placed coconuts and flowers, and then sat beside it day and night chanting Hindu Vedic prayers, and keeping a sacred fire burning.

Many of the thousands of people who rose before dawn today to make sure of a "ringside seat" at the disinterment obviously believed that Swami had bitten off more than he could chew. They watched tensely as his followers hacked away the cement with picks.

Some men crawled down to the coffin with blankets. They lifted out the Swami—still in his Yogic trance—putting him on a dais where all could see him. They then slowly massaged his head, arms, and body, until he opened his eyes, looked slowly around—and smiled.

Dr. Jal Ruston Vakil, of Bombay, a noted heart specialist, who received his medical degree at London University, immediately examined Swami.

Swami's pulse was beating *eight to the minute,* said Vakil, and his blood pressure was 1.16 over 80, which was normal for a person who had fasted for many days. He noted that his respiration was slow, but that otherwise he was normal in every respect.

Other doctors who were present as interested spectators said that a normal person could only have lived two hours in the crypt in which Swami had been entombed. It was Swami's sixth successful *samadi*—the name by which the Yogic trance is known. In a *samadi* the Yogi has complete control of all his muscles—so that he can stop his respiration completely at will.

This is the second entombment which this correspondent has seen and he can state that the feat was not a magician's trick but a genuine demonstration of the powers the cult of Yoga can produce.

Swami is held in reverence by the thousands who have visited his "tomb" during the past few days. No tickets were sold—no money was taken—it was simply a religious ceremony. After coming out of the trance today Swami sat on the dais while parents brought their little children up to him so that they might touch him. Many foreigners were among the crowd and they simply gaped in wonder.

Another report of the same case was published in *The Times of India,* which added, "Acclaiming the feat as a miraculous deed, Mr. C. B. Velkar, Presidency Magistrate, Bombay, told the huge gathering that the Yogi was as fit as ever and could challenge anybody for a mile-long race."

What is the secret of this amazing power of breath-suspension? One fact is evident—during his lonely vigil, the Yogi is in an abnormal state. By a supreme effort of concentration he induces a condition which, I suggest, resembles hibernation—a phenomenon common in subhuman life. Many animals have the ability to live without breath. When, after the long winter sleep, they return to their normal state, respiration is resumed in the usual manner. A hibernating hedgehog will give no sign of breathing. To all appearances, respiration has completely ceased. Touch it even lightly and it will resume breathing and continue doing so for a short period, later lapsing again into the breathless state.

That hibernating animals do not breathe at all is

suggested by various tests: a hedgehog, when awake, may be drowned inside three minutes, but in the hibernated state it has been suspended under water for as long as twenty-two minutes, without injury. Hibernating ducks have lived for four hours in carbon dioxide—an atmosphere instantly fatal to their normal condition.

All too little is known about this extraordinary phenomenon of hibernation, though animals in less cold climates pass the whole winter in that condition. (A similar state, known as "aestivation," is assumed by animals in very hot latitudes, during the summer months.)

It would seem, therefore, that although breathing is essential to sustain life, it can be suspended for long periods under certain conditions. Following our principle of analyzing in detail the simple, natural phenomena of life, let us now see if this function of respiration can be extended in the same way as relaxation and contraction.

Breathing is a two-way activity, involving inhalation and exhalation. The amount of air you normally take into your lungs is governed by a number of circumstances. Among these are sex, height, weight, and, above all, the attention given to the breathing act. Other factors which affect the intake of air are the posture assumed by the body, the nature of the surrounding atmosphere, and whether or not you are under any physical or emotional stress.

Normally the volume of air taken in and given out in ordinary respiration is about 20 cubic inches.

However, this volume can be forcibly increased to 100 or even 130 cubic inches—so we have an ample margin for expansion.

Further, your organism is at no time entirely without air. Having apparently cleared the lungs of all air, there still remains a certain amount of "residual air"—that is to say, the quantity of air left in the chest after the most complete expiration. This residual air ranges in volume from 100 to 130 cubic inches. It may be that the Yogi master of breath-control subsists on this narrow reserve when he is buried alive for hours or days.

Now examine what actually happens when the act of respiration takes place. The air you breathe passes into the lungs and is absorbed, via the delicate membrane of the lung cells, into the blood. Air, then, is a food—actually, the most important food known to man. Other items in his diet he can eliminate or substitute, but there is no survival without this fundamental item. Strange that people can be so fastidious about the food they chew and yet they are content to swallow any kind of air, however stale or devitalized!

Breath is indispensable to all growth—far, far more important than ordinary food. And fresh, clean air is more nutritious than old, stale air.

To continue with human respiration, when oxygen commingles with the blood, a great life-giving cycle of changes is begun. First the act of breathing propels air along to the heart. From here it is pumped through the arteries to the capillaries and fed into the bodily tissues. Thus is your body continually "fed" with new draughts of oxygen. Now, the tissues, having thrived on the oxygen, excrete a waste product which we call carbon dioxide. This waste is passed back into the blood and so the carbon dioxide returns, via the veins, to the lungs, from where it is finally expelled in the outgoing breath.

This twofold operation constitutes what we call "breathing." Observe that the pace of the operation is never fixed. When you are under pressure, your breathing will step up automatically to maintain the extra level of energy needed. This pressure may be either physical or emotional. The average adult inspires .25 cubic feet every minute when resting. When under stress, that figure will be multiplied perhaps eight times. Simultaneously, the amount of carbon dioxide expelled will be correspondingly increased. (While resting it ranges from ½ a cubic foot per hour to 5 cubic feet per hour when under stress.)

Now it transpires that the *deeper* you breathe, the higher the percentage of carbon dioxide expelled. Close study of the respiratory processes proved to me that a little time given daily to breathing exercises of a special type would substantially improve the condition of the blood and tissues—and hence, over-all physical and mental health. I observed that the average man and woman neglect the breathing act. Not only is there failure to adequately feed the lung cells, but the lungs themselves are not given sufficient exercise.

Here, then, was an opportunity to put into effect

the principle of Deep Contraction. It boils down to this advice: *Don't allow your lungs, through lack of usage, to lose their elasticity.* How often recently have you given them an energizing stretch? Probably only when forced to do so by nature.' (This happens in coughing, sneezing, sighing, laughing, yawning—a fit of hiccoughs may be nature's way of giving lethargic lungs a necessary airing.)

So far we have considered respiration as if it were a self-contained, independent, process. But that is not the case. You have seen how difficult it is to study inhaling without taking into account what happens when exhaling, how physical exertions and mental and emotional states can affect respiration, how the condition of the blood is influenced by breathing and how the bodily tissues are fed by oxygen, and—finally —how all these influence your general condition of health.

However primitive it may be, breathing is certainly not a simple physical action. It is also an emotional and mental affair. And because it overlaps these three planes—the physical, the emotional, the mental—why not have a breathing technique which would give a boost to each?

This is precisely what I have evolved in the routine known as Dynamic Breathing. It is a simple health-giving technique which can be practiced by both sexes and at any age. Even those who are prevented from carrying out the Deep Contraction exercises should be able to practice Dynamic Breathing. It will be found especially helpful by women. Men normally do tend to exercise the abdominal walls when breath-

ing. With women, chest expansion is more pronounced—due partly to woman's different anatomy
and the constriction of the chest by wearing corsets.

Dynamic Breathing involves a slow, sustained intake of air (via the nose). Simultaneously with this
respiration, you learn to push out the abdominal area.
(This enables you to fill the lower part of the lungs
first. The pressure thus exerted on the abdominal wall
has been found to stimulate organs concerned with
digestion and elimination. After a week or two's practice, there will be a noticeable improvement in these
latter functions.)

When the lungs have been slowly filled to capacity,
the air is exhaled, *again through the nose*. This act of
exhalation is also performed at a slow tempo.

Although the traditional Yoga breathing exercises
specified that the breath, when first drawn in, should
be held for a certain period, and also that there should
be a period of breath-suspension between two acts of
respiration, neither of these pauses enter into my
technique of Dynamic Breathing. Though breath
retention and suspension are, indeed, an integral part
of ancient Yogic discipline for subjugating the physical body, certain dangers attend them, so that they
cannot be universally commended.

On the other hand, slow nasal inhalation and
exhalation can be performed without risk or strain
by all unaffected with lung disease. There is no need
to hold the breath. One may even, if one chooses, rest
and breathe normally between two Dynamic Breaths.
But if only five minutes or so be spent in the performance of this slow, sustained or, as I call it, Dynamic

Breathing, first thing each morning and last thing each evening—it will soon improve vitality. For there is more involved in the principle of Dynamic Breathing than the simple physical operation of slowly inflating the lungs and, by the depth of respiration, massaging the abdominal area. I found that the mental suggestions that could be allied to this exercise were equally important.

Recall the experiments of Maynow, a seventeenth-century British chemist and physiologist. Maynow conducted a number of investigations which showed that life is supported not by air alone but by a "more active and subtle part of it." This subtle constituent he considered a basic necessity of life. He suggested that the lungs separated it from the atmosphere and passed it into the blood stream. At first this view was naturally received with ridicule. A century later Priestley and Lavoisier gave it respectability by naming the extra constituent "oxygen" and restating Maynow's hypothesis is purely physical terms.

As usual, the materialistic explanation was readily accepted. But I suspect that it does not entirely dispose of Maynow's *spiritus igneo-aereus,* the name he gave to the hidden property which he had discovered in the atmosphere. In Maynow's day it was commonly believed by physiologists that the purpose of breathing was to "cool the heart." Not only did Maynow expose this superstition—he was the first man to regard exhalation as part of the excretory process.

My contention is that this English chemist of the seventeenth century not only lived a hundred years before his time: he was actually several centuries ahead. Though oxygen is an hypothesis freely accepted today, Maynow's *spiritus igneo-aereus* (that which was not air but a "more active and subtle part of it") is, I believe, only partly covered by the theory of oxygen. Oxygen may be the outer garment, as it were, of a still more subtle force—the force which the Yogis identified as *"prana."* As yet no instrument has been invented by science to measure *prana,* but that does not say *prana* has no existence. Nor will it explain why for four or five thousand years—long, long before the modern discovery of oxygen proved air to be a very complex thing—there flourished this strong conviction that the atmosphere contained a latent, vital power. The ancient Hindu theory is that all physical and mental manifestations are dependent upon *prana.* Further, the amount of this vital force drawn into the system can be increased by exploiting man's greatest gift—his power of imagination. In the same way as the physical oxygen is absorbed through the lungs and passed, by means of the blood stream, to all parts of the body, so *prana* can be drawn from the atmosphere and distributed throughout the body. The nervous system is the line of communication for distributing the pranic force. In fact, says the Yogi, *prana* is automatically inspired in our everyday breathing, albeit in limited form. But the amount can be increased consciously by concentrating on certain power centers located at strategic points throughout the body. These centers are called *chakras.* They are positioned at the crown of the head, the brow, the throat, heart, solar plexus, and elsewhere. And to "awaken" them a number of curious exercises were invented.

Such Oriental elaboration need not concern us here. But, conversely, we should not waste time "debunking" the whole idea of *prana*. Until modern science invents an instrument sufficiently delicate to chart it, the existence of *prana* may be hotly disputed by Western "know-alls." However, as so much of Yoga which was previously rejected has now been verified by recent scientific advances, this last dispute is relatively unimportant. What matters is whether the ordinary layman, given a certain *prana*-breathing routine, can actually obtain help from it.

People who practice Dynamic Breathing for a week or so are unanimous in stating that their energy, stamina, and general well-being have been fortified. The secret is to couple the power of visualization (call it imagination, it matters not) to this very slow, controlled breathing sequence. During the period of inspiration you should form a mental picture of fresh energy being drawn into the body. When exhaling, see yourself pouring out from your system all fatigue, ill health, and depression.

Dynamic Breathing calls for mental and physical acts simultaneously. Try it and Deep Relaxation, when fatigued or low in spirit, and your whole outlook will be immediately changed. You will better understand, then, the scriptural allusion to God "breathing" into man the "breath of life." Obviously the Old Testament writer knew and practiced it.

What is responsible for this new "life" which is imparted by Dynamic Breathing? Is it the sheer physical exercise given to the lungs by these long, controlled respirations? Is it just autosuggestion? Or is there a separate energy source which can be tapped by visualization—the process whereby one creates mental pictures? It may be the interplay of all these things together that accounts for the energy released in Dynamic Breathing. I know and care not. More relevant than theories are the results reported by those who practice this new form of breathing exercise.

Mass-Observation analyzed 1,000 reports from students who had actually done Dynamic Breathing. Almost all said they felt their lungs were better for the exercise—more fit and strong; 80 per cent said that the sinus passage was cleared during Dynamic Breathing; 50 per cent said that the nostrils and breathing passages were cleared. These are very impressive figures. But they are not the whole story.

Other benefits claimed were "greater alertness," "fitness," "easier breathing," "relief from catarrh," from constipation, indigestion and other popular evils. This is not surprising considering how Dynamic Breathing massages the internal organs of the digestive system.

Take some concrete examples: C. H. D., reported

"The Yogism breathing exercises have resulted in lessening catarrh, regular bowel action and clearer thinking. I am back to 100 per cent fitness."

B. W. wrote:

"All weariness leaves my body, after doing the Yogism breathing. My head is clear and I feel new blood in my veins. You have created a new man from a wreck—I never thought it possible."

A Brazilian student—W. C.—is another who singled out Dynamic Breathing because of the cleansing effect upon the lungs and breathing passages.

"After this exercise," he wrote, "I feel as if all worries and anxieties have left me."

More localized benefits are frequently reported. For example, J. F. wrote:

"My waist line seems smaller and although my chest measurement was 44 inches the diaphragm is more supple and elastic."

Even so he was more interested in the neutral stimulus experienced—in his case,

"more energy, better memory, self-confidence."

T. A. H. put it similarly:

"I have experienced a refreshing and beneficial sensation from the Yogism breathing. I can breathe more clearly and freely—most wonderful, this exercise. I have become a happier and more alert person."

These letters are drawn at random from a stack of similar correspondence before me as I write, for almost every Yogism student reports immediate benefits from practicing Dynamic Breathing. It rarely fails to soothe the nerves, bestowing a greater sense of harmony and self-possession.

Supposing these people—88 per cent of all who have ever tried Dynamic Breathing—are victims of imagination, what of it? At the worst, they are only using their imagination constructively instead of allowing it to run wild. They are using it to give themselves a happier, healthier, more vigorous life. Surely that is worth having!

As it happens, I know imagination is *not* the answer. First of all, the physical exercise involved in practical Dynamic Breathing cannot be disputed. Most middle-age people have weak abdominals. Their intestinal muscles are soon strengthened by doing Dynamic Breathing. As the air is inspired, the digestive organs —liver and pancreas—are pushed out against the abdominal walls and gently massaged. With expiration, contraction takes place and so the good work of stretching and massaging continues. Internal organs concerned with elimination—organs which normally become flaccid and inactive with the advance of years —are given a good shaking. Muscles which are weakened by disuse are rejuvenated.

Then, too, during Dynamic Breathing, strongly oxygenized blood is pumped to the uttermost extremities of the body. And excretory action is facilitated by the exhalation of waste in the form of carbon dioxide. Other waste is passed through the sweat glands of the skin. (Certain Yogic breathing exercises are so intensive that they make the body drip with perspiration. They have no place in my system and should not be practiced without supervision.)

Stated thus, in purely physical terms, the Dynamic Breathing technique is unquestionably beneficial. But when it is carried out imaginatively—when, that is to say, thought is harnessed to physical action and a sincere, creative effort is made to imbibe more of this vital life force in the shape of *prana*—then it becomes a more potent thing.

Make your own first experiments in Dynamic Breathing as rhythmical and smooth as possible—that is to say, take approximately the same time to draw in the breath as to pass it out of the body. (Normally inhalation involves a shorter movement than exhalation, but you should strive to equalize them.) Aim at a regular rhythm. As you breathe in, *visualize* your limbs as hollow tubes, through which the health-giving *prana* is being drawn into your body. Picture this energy swelling all over your body, submerging your whole physique at the height of the inhalation. In the reverse action, exhale as slowly and in as controlled fashion as possible. Visualize the fatigue and exhaustion passing out of your system along with the expiring breath. You know that, physically, you are getting rid of poison—banish the fatigue and exhaustion with it.

Having indulged for some minutes in this highly dramatized breathing technique, finish with what we call the "Cleansing Breath." To do this you should again inhale slowly through the nose and, when you feel that your lungs are fully extended, expel the air suddenly—again through the nose. This time you exhale with a quick inward jerk of the abdomen. Do this cleansing breath two or three times (not more), and you will experience a "tonic" and bracing effect.

With the Dynamic Breathing session, your daily Yogism program for long life and happiness is almost completed. Remember, you have already done a short period of Deep Relaxation. This was followed by its complementary—Deep Contraction. After the natural, sustained stretches, you will want to rest. So Dynamic Breathing has its place. A sense of harmony and balance is soon created. Only one more thing remains to be achieved. You must now learn to exercise your *will*.

CHAPTER 6

Step 4 to Liberation:
Dynamic Concentration

WE ARE ALL influenced by our surroundings. Some of us, however, have found it easier than others, to set a limit to the influence of environment. Unless a man becomes *self*-conscious (not in the sense of shyness but rather in awareness of his separate existence as an individual), he is very much dominated by outward circumstances. Men called for military service may come from a sensitive, cultured environment yet quickly coarsen in the cruder atmosphere of the barrackroom. Swear words, which they would have been scandalized to hear at home, soon slip unwittingly from their own lips. A new outlook is formed. They act differently because they think differently. And they think differently because their concentration is focused on different things.

The Yogis recognized the immense importance of concentration. They drew the inference than men could be changed for the better, just as easily as for the worse, by concentrating on new *Samskaras* (or impressions). Two people faced with the same situation will react differently. Why? One will see only some facts, one others. Most Western people give little or no thought to mental training of any kind. Many will say they can't concentrate—which, of course, is rubbish. Everyone, whether he is aware of it or not, exercises the power of concentration all day long. Alas, from the point of view of mental well-being and success in life, this power is employed only in a reactionary sense. That is to say, attention is pivoted on whatever outward stimulation catches the fancy. There are, of course, lots of people ready to saturate you with the wrong sort of mental associations—to tell you that you are no good, to frighten you, threaten you, bully you. If you are unfortunate enough to be submitted to anything like a systematic bombardment of this type, your morale may be soon undermined, *unless you concentrate on something else*.

Clearly the first step to mental freedom is to cultivate this power of concentration—to select your attitude to life rather than accept the first ideas (often detrimental) that come into your head. These first ideas are generally due to outside influences, although sometimes they are modified by your own physical condition. Oh! those mornings when you wake with a "liver"—those days when you view the whole world with a jaundiced eye! No doubting on what you are concentrating then! You are "tuned in" to the wave length of your own bad health, the previous day's mistakes, the vileness of your antagonists, and all the other odds that are ranged against you.

Now you can make your long life a great deal happier if you resolve to bring this irresponsible thinking under restraint. In other words, you must pre-select the targets of your attention and so rivet your thoughts upon them as to rule out all disruptive associations. There is a way of doing this and the early Yogis had the formula. How sweeping and potent that formula could be is demonstrated by the Indian fakir's tremendous power over the body. To succeed in suspending breath for several days, or halting the beat of the heart, or do the hundred and one other extraordinary feats performed by Hatha Yogis must demand concentration of an intensive kind. Its cultivation takes years.

Happily, as civilized life has little use for such extreme powers, no comparable effort is required on your part. To develop the concentration you need is a comparatively simple process. Nevertheless, it, too, involves some exertion, particularly in the initial stage.

It means checking emotional reactions—becoming "wise" to instinctive feelings of hatred, jealousy, indignation, and so on—and substituting your own carefully chosen and preferred attitudes.

The first mental impediment to Dynamic Concentration—as I have called this process—is restlessness. Instead of allowing your attention to be propelled this way and that by the ephemeral *stimuli* of the moment, Dynamic Concentration means preventing yourself from being immersed in the passing phenomena of life. This attitude of withdrawal or detachment is not easy to acquire; but, if attempted assiduously, the state—a truly blessed one—*can* be cultivated even by the most erratic and nervous temperaments in course of time. It is certainly worth cultivating, too. A restless personality can never be healthy. Nothing plays such havoc with the nervous system as a fitful, agitated mind.

The average man in the street is a creature of automatic reflexes. If he is fortunate in his associations, he thrives. If, however, he is surrounded by gloom, criticism, tyranny, or worse, his thoughts will automatically add fuel to the flames that are consuming him. Only to the extent that he thinks *for himself* can he become independent.

It may, perhaps, be argued that he can never be wholly free, because of the numerous subconscious *stimuli* which enter into the thinking process. That is true—but why be a complete slave to automatic reactions? Here is where civilized education slips up. It teaches everything—except how to think. Education is almost entirely abstract. Children are not taught to *live*. Instead, they are carefully schooled in herd reaction. One day our modern psychologists may give less attention to neurotic problems and devise new ways of developing mental independence. Or perhaps they may be employed by a dictator to make human responses still more automatic than at present. The study of Yoga shows that this could indeed be done, and the prospects are truly frightening.

Five thousand years ago Yoga was defined as "the complete mastery of the mind and emotions." This is actually the first statement Patanjali makes in the famous *Sutras,* which constitutes the Bible of Yoga. Not until this complete mastery was realized, he taught, could an individual really become "aware of himself." Ordinarily, men are so closely identified with their own confused picture of life as to be completely lost and absorbed in it. They develop opinions and "values" which are merely projections of their existing environment. They arrive at "conclusions" which are simply the sum of routine habits, traditions, manners, and so forth. The whole of their lives is based on a "thinking" process which only reflects the feelings and sensations they have most recently experienced.

Yoga sought to make the individual conscious of his presence as a *unit separate and distinct from the outward manifestations of life.* It sought to disentangle his personality from these confused and conflicting impressions. Long before Freud and Adler named the craving for self-expression, the instinct for self-preservation, etc., as motivating and spread human life, Yoga had passed this milestone and spread beyond. Indeed, present-day psychologists are still struggling to understand man's mind by inferring things from its behavior. Naturally, the deeper they thrust, the more difficult, if not impossible, it becomes for them to dissociate their own prejudices and fancies from the investigation.

The Yogis proceeded quite differently—and more directly—to self-knowledge. Through the development of intense concentration and meditation, the individual student was taught immediate knowledge *within himself.* He knew well enough how responsive he was to environment and past experience. But he knew, too, that the chain of automatic reaction which normally passes for thought could be severed by the action of the will. Thinking and feeling could be regulated and controlled at their source. Thus, a man could, if he chose, change his whole picture of the world. And the first move in this new, better direction, was to learn to think of *one thing at a time*. In other words—real concentration.

Thus, by "taking thought," it was found possible to subdue a restless mind, pacify a nervous disposition, and to cultivate what I call "Self-faith." This meant that the Yogi began to live virtually a new life. To achieve this end, rigorous mental disciplines were practiced. They need not concern us today. Sufficient to say they would be impracticable to follow under modern conditions.

The objective of the ancient Yogi was *Samyama*, the deepest form of meditation, in which he enjoyed the ecstasy of God-union. This ultimate form of meditation was reached by two steps. First, *Dharana* or concentration so acute that the student focused on one thing only, to the exclusion of all others. (This may seem easy enough but, in fact, it is extremely difficult and requires long practice.) The second step was *Dhyana,* a state of contemplation wherein control of thought and feeling becomes perfect and absolute. Thus apprenticed, the student finally reaches the advanced state of *Samadhi* or God-union—a state of infinite bliss.

However, our hard-headed Western approach bids us be more realistic and practical. We want to deepen our powers of concentration and avoid wasteful activity. It is sufficient reason. If, later on, we should experience beneficial side-effects, so much the better.

To make our concentration power more potent, then, we must begin by analyzing our own thought processes. They fashion, to quite a large extent, the picture we form of life. It is continually changing. We make the colors brighter or darker, as we choose. *By altering our attitudes here and now, we can also exert a direct influence on our future, because tomorrow's deeds have their origin today.*

These basic facts are so simple that no one attaches importance to them. We accept them, pass on . . . and forget. But it is just here precisely that Yogism bids us pause. If by regulating our thought habits (in other words, by developing our concentration), we can make something new of our present lives and something different of our future prospects, we ought to be up and doing. We ought to cease living like robots.

To change the thinking habits of a lifetime is, of course, no easy feat. Concentration is the only key to unlock this door. Luckily we all possess this key, though it has become rusty through neglect. Of course, it is a terribly difficult key to use. You say to yourself "I will do this thing". . . and soon your attention wavers, and you find yourself doing something else. (Often, doing nothing!)

"Dynamic Concentration" is the name I gave to the Yogism technique for shaping and sharpening this mighty power that lies latent in every mind— "Dynamic" because the concentration we develop has a sweep, energy, and force of unbelievable dimensions. With Dynamic Concentration, you can pin your mind to any task, however difficult and unpleasant, long enough to make a success of it.

Most people attempt to improve their concentration by coupling it to big things. New Year's resolutions are a fair example. You resolve you will give up smoking, swearing, exaggerating, etc. (why are New Year's resolutions generally things we will *not* do?). Then events intervene and you forget your resolution. The "will" was there, but not the more important ingredient — Dynamic Concentration. Such concentration is singlepointed and sustained—singlepointed in the sense that it actually pins the mind to one thing at a time and it holds it there long enough for that thing to become a reality.

Normally we are far too impressionable. Our attention darts hither and thither as we pass first under one influence and then under another. By practicing the Dynamic Concentration formula, you will first train your mind to check wayward and roving tendencies in regard to simple things. It follows, then, that you will soon be better equipped to tackle major things, because your previous training will have made your mind more supple and responsive.

The formula is to focus your thought—all your thought—on one pinpoint, to begin with. It can, indeed, be quite literally the point of a pin: nothing better. Or, if you wish, the "target" may be the pattern of a handkerchief or the design of a small piece of wallpaper, or a single letter on a page or a symbol drawn on paper. It can be anything—the simpler, the better—but it must be *one definite object*.

Now, just for thirty seconds, focus your thought on this target, whatever its form. Not, mark you, on the impressions called up in your mind by simply "dwelling" on it. That kind of concentration is not one-pointed.

You may think thirty seconds is a short time for this exercise but when you practice it, the period will seem an eternity at first. Remember, you must nail down the whole thinking mechanism so that all your attention and all your imagination and all your consciousness are utterly, completely, monopolized by one thing. To begin with, this will prove quite impossible. But it is possible with practice, and so you must just try again—and again—until you have exhausted your mind. This means that you will initially abandon the exercise after only a few minutes' practice.

Do not then be discouraged! Try again tomorrow, and the next day. *Every day for a month,* give yourself this regular daily "target practice." Suddenly, it will be easier . . . but not until you have tried quite a few times and not at all unless you make the practice a daily routine. Everyone, surely, can afford the handful of minutes required each day. Don't excuse yourself on the grounds of being "too busy." Don't give in simply because at first you find it tiresome. It is bound to be tiresome—because never before in your life have you asked your mind to think of one thing, and one thing only, for a period of several minutes.

What happens during these brief exercises in Dynamic Concentration? The mind, which is normally a storm-tossed sea, is suddenly stilled. The churning waves are momentarily smoothed. If the tempest of thought which continually rages in your mind can be stilled for a split second only, it can, remember, be stilled for a much longer period. But it requires practice.

At the moment your mind resembles the control room of a big organization. This room is continually fed with messages and signals conveyed via the sense organs. You have become so adept at recording, deciphering and coordinating all this data that you are hardly aware of the strain on your nervous system as one set of data is replaced by another, and new impressions replace old ones.

In some people this perpetual flow of feelings and ideas occasionally gets out of hand. They become bad-tempered, excitable, changeable, irresponsible. And no wonder! For all who do not practice (knowingly or unknowingly) the art of Dynamic Concentration have to face a subconscious background of tension that is terribly exhausting. Such people become jumpy and agitated, they do foolish things, indulge in silly prattle, harbor stupid fears, and don't do what they ought to do because they are frightened or have forgotten.

When you apply Dynamic Concentration by fixing the attention on an insignificant target, you develop, in course of time, mental control of a new order. You can choose a mental wave length, so to speak, *and remain on that wave length all the day, whatever happens.* You pre-select an outlook (and consequently, through that attitude, you influence to a large extent your actual experience of life). This power of discrimination makes all the difference between a happy day and an unhappy one, for people so "pre-tuned" can encounter ill will and misfortune without being hurt. No amount of jealousy or envy can affect them. Life is not only happier; it becomes more purposeful. Once the mind is dynamically trained to think along cheerful, constructive lines, everything that happens merely becomes another lever to assist future accomplishment.

Without such Dynamic Concentration, what happens? Morose and doubtful acquaintances discourage. Critical and skeptical acquaintances arouse self-questions. Fractious and interfering associates provoke indiscretions. So the central objective of the day is lost sight of and all becomes lost—in a maze of futility. Perhaps tomorrow you try again. But still nothing is realized if your associations are wrong. Not until a fortunate combination of circumstances leaves your path serenely clear can you make the desired advance. Such fortunate combinations of circumstances are seldom encountered, however—for other people's minds are as restless as your own. They, too, are wavering and undecided, and so you interfere with and thwart one another.

Apart altogether from the practical advantages of everyday applications of Dynamic Concentration, there is a subtle gain that has already been hinted. The practice will enable you to stop projecting *yourself* into the details of daily living. Through Dynamic Concentration you will cultivate a more detached attitude—and this by itself is a means of evading the worst pangs of unkindness and evil. Normally you experience life at close range—so close, in fact, that a stray word can cause injured feelings or a careless action cause a quarrel. This propinquity is unwise: for the good things, no less than the unpleasant things, excite you *too much.*

If we consider how his emotions and actions fluctuate throughout the day, in response to each new sensory impression received, it is extraordinary that the average person's health is no worse than it is. His nervous system is subjected to much unnecessary strain and punishment, which the cultivation of a detached attitude entirely avoids.

It may now be evident why the person who practices Dynamic Concentration has a better chance of long life and happiness. He is no longer the victim of every fleeting emotion. By setting his life to a wave length of his own choice, he gains more "say" over his future. He acquires an inner poise and purposefulness which instantly communicates itself to others. His face looks younger. His habits and gestures are more economic and quiet. His work improves, as he learns to bend all his powers on one thing at a time. He sidesteps the tension created by conflicting interests. Above all, when conditions are against him, he does not lose his head. He avoids being unduly perturbed because he does not submerge his personality in what happens outside. Having cultivated a detached attitude, he is better placed to resist the shocks and disappointments of life; and since he is not floored by them, he can take quick remedial action. Worry and fluster, for him, are shades of the past. He stands back and looks *at* life instead of being flustered by it. What a saving in pain, disappointment, and high tension!

With the development of Dynamic Concentration, one becomes a more coordinated, better poised personality; without it, a bundle of automatic reactions. One type has a sense of direction; the other flounders where chance associations lead him. One has courage and independence, the other is obsessed by fear and submission. One accepts fortune and misfortune with equal detachment; the other is a creature of moods dictated by each day's fate.

Those who have actually practiced Dynamic Concentration know from experience that this formula works. Having worked for them, it can work for you also. In fact, it is probably already working for you—but the wrong way round. For it is a fact that, although concentration on the conscious plane is an exceedingly arduous task, it is happening all the time on the subconscious level without the least effort on your part. Many physical ailments are brought about in the first place, by subconscious anxiety and tension. Some fear or tension dynamically seizes the mind, setting up irritations that manifest themselves as sickness. Modern medicine accepts this fact. There is overwhelming proof that serious illnesses can be simulated by mental suggestion, and inner tension.*

* Findings simulating those of organic heart disease can be produced in some normal people under hypnosis, according to a report that comes from the University of California Medical School. Five normal students were the subjects. Heart function was determined with the electrocardiograph. Under hypnosis the students' hearts all could be made to beat faster after suggestion. When anxiety and anger were suggested, the electrocardiogram of one student showed

Consider how Dynamic Concentration works in illness. Whatever the cause of their disease, most patients look to a doctor for cure. He is expected to prescribe, minister, and do all that is needful, while the patient lies back and concentrates on his ailment. No wonder we need powerful drugs to shock the patient out of his state of self-hypnosis. Recovery really begins once he—the patient—assumes some responsibility for getting better, instead of unloading the whole onus on the doctor's shoulders. It will help still more when he discovers that the healing must take place *within himself*. Doctors can begin the healing work, but at some point the patient himself must take over and complete the task.

This Dynamic Concentration is a medicine to be self-administered. That is why patients don't like it. It requires personal effort. It asks the sick to "focus" on something remote from their illness at a time when the latter is a subject of absorbing interest!

So, now, we have seen many ways in which this dynamic power of concentration can be harnessed to improve the standard of life. We have seen how it can short-circuit those damaging, wasteful daily conflicts which previously took us off our course. We have seen how it can release us from the strain of unnecessary tension and the pangs of unnecessary disappointment. We know that when we develop it we shall be free of the welter of confusion, distraction, and conflict which is the subconscious background of

changes like those found in true organic heart disease. The findings have a bearing on some of the difficulties of diagnosing true heart disease.—*The New York Times.*

normal living. We know we can reduce this strain, cut out the manifold irrelevancies. Improvement in health is our first gain. Skill at one's job, clearness in one's general perception and grasp of detail, fortitude in seeing through to finality a pre-determined plan whatever happens—these are other advantages.

It may seem fantastic that so much can follow from such simple daily exercises. If so, it is only because you are still ignorant of the chaotic nature of your mental life. With thoughts running wild all over the place, and control of automatic reactions almost entirely absent, it is natural one should doubt that so much can follow from so little.

Yet is there really so little involved in these Dynamic Concentration exercises? Unfortunately, no. The exercises read simply, but they are difficult to carry out. Yet every time you succeed in reducing the number of thoughts in your mind, you will be given extra control over the future. Ultimately you will discover that *what the mind dwells on, it must become.* This discovery is not new really. Nor is it exclusively Yoga. Such knowledge has been known to man in every age—knowledge so true, so obvious, its full significance was never grasped. How often again shall we need to be told that "As a man thinketh in his heart, so is he."?

Of course, this power over thought can be carried to extremes. Which accounts for the ecstasy or "God-union" experienced by the Yogi in his lonely mountain retreat. He gives his whole life to meditation—long before dawn he begins his daily practice, and he continues in deep abstractions for hours at a stretch. He has so checked the feverish activity of the mind that one thought, and one thought only, animates his mind—reunion with God. The Christian authority for this mystical absorption is contained in numerous familiar texts—"Be still and know that I am God," for instance. The Yogi certainly knows how to be still, in his mind, in order to open his heart to God.

But life sweeps on at too fast a pace, here in the West, for such intensive, prolonged, and abstract concentration. It is enough if we can master this act in partial and, as we say, "more practical," form. God-intoxication is an experience which most of us will be content to read about. Everyday affairs press in upon us, outlawing mysticism. We would like to live more evenly, more happily, and for a longer period of time. And if we apply the magic of Dynamic Concentration, we can.

CHAPTER 7

How to Eat Longer, Live Younger

THE further the human animal "advances" from a natural environment, the greater become his complications.

Nowhere will you see this truth more strikingly evidenced than in man's eating habits.

Time was when he fed on fresh, living foods. Most of his day was devoted to obtaining them. And when he ate, he lay down and relaxed. He may not have known that this helped to digest his food. Still, it worked.

But life advanced—and became more complicated. Succeeding generations planned and built to make everything more "efficient." The getting and preparation of food became a detail relegated to specialists. Now, instead of every man feeding himself, he employed others to feed him.

The transition was inevitable. Great cities had been raised above the good productive earth. There were now many more things to do, and less time to do them in. So it became "natural" to entrust experts with the production, preparation, and distribution of food. Today a multitude of these specialists serve your every meal.

For your pleasure, O powerful reader, these slaves who attend your table are active from dawn until dusk. They are working for you from the moment the seed is planted in the ground. The very earth is *fortified* with chemical manures. As soon as the crop begins to appear, it is *cleansed* with chemical sprays. The harvest is then *canned, cartoned, tinned, frozen,* or otherwise *preserved* for your convenience. To entice your palate, it has been *flavored*. To please the eye *colored*. To satisfy the skeptical, *"improved."* And finally, may Heaven forgive us, it is scientifically *naturalized*—in a nice, hygienic, modern factory.

Labor-saving, it may be, to have your food served up in this manner. But is it good for you? Is it really progress?

As if in answer to the doubts already forming in your mind, a new host of experts spring up to assure you. No sooner do you rush from the table, hurrying to your next appointment with the last bite only just swallowed, than they are there, confronting you with questions. Lack energy? Liver upset? Need a pick-me-up? No, no, my dear sir or madam, we don't sell medicines. That's out of fashion now. What you need, what you really need, to keep you fit and well, is a good strong daily dose of Vitamins!

Welcome the Dieticians! Good, worthy men and women, possessing infinite skill. A democratic lot, too, for they hold views of surprising variance. You may question the precise mathematics by which they label the calorie-content of your meals. But down, deep down, you know they have the advantage of you. For in fact you *do* instinctively feel short of Vitamin A. Every adult, you have read, needs 6,000 units daily. You are sure you are not getting that amount. Vitamins B, C, and D, too—you should have 600 of the latter every day and you can't quite believe you are enjoying a full ration.

The complications are growing! And still only a handful of these essential Vitamins are known! Wait until you read about the other Vitamins science is still engaged in discovering. Then you really will have something to worry about: perhaps a different kind of Vitamin pill will be recommended for every course of every meal.

The Dieticians are here and, make no mistake, they are here to stay. If we did not need them, they would not be around.

So long as we eat devitalized and often dead foods we shall need the services of these vital and often lively Dieticians. They are indispensable. Of course it's confusing that some of them advocate a mere 600 units of Vitamin A daily, while others insist on a full 50,000. A small detail like this is one of the things Progress may be relied on to smooth out soon! In the meanwhile, the important feature is that the Dieticians are making you Vitamin-conscious. Because in course of time you may then get round to doing something about this question of Vitamins.

You may even decide to take them naturally, through the mouth, *in living food.*

Vitamin A, for instance, which enables the body

cells to resist infection: it is your first defense against disease. Don't go to your chemist for Vitamin A unless you are in a very bad way and need urgent "crisis" treatment. Thank the Dietician who seems so interested in selling capsules and just have a quiet talk with your grocer. Ask him to let you have more beet greens, kale, turnip tops, and broccoli, for leafy vegetables are Nature's source of Vitamin A, and Nature's source is the best and most economical source of supply. Dairy produce is another source of Vitamin A: milk, butter, eggs. Fruits, too, especially apricot, supply it. And so, too, in the meat family, do liver and lamb. Whether or not you favor a vegetarian diet, see that your meals include fresh vegetables and dairy produce whenever you can.

As you know, there is not one but a whole series of Vitamin B. This Vitamin group greatly influences digestion. As digestion, in turn, regulates the amount of nourishment extracted from any food, quite clearly the Vitamin B series rank high in importance. The most wonderful natural source of this series is wheat. Yet I know of no food so badly treated.

Consider what happens to the common grain of wheat. Once it is grown, it is beheaded, then threshed, ground, washed, sieved, decimated, mixed, kneaded, and baked. . . . Somehow, the dynamic spark of life contained in the long-suffering wheat grain survives all these dreadful machinations. Even then it is not finished with. In the final processing, its natural minerals, bran, and semolina, are *removed*. Then chalk and nitrogen trichloride are *added*. The result is flour—but don't blame the mills for it. Or the wheat crop. The living wheat germ just must be discarded if we are to feed large communities, for to do this flour must be stored in great dumps for long periods. A living natural flour would not keep, so a dead flour has to be manufactured. In course of time you cultivate a liking for this devitalized white flour. Worse still, you begin to suspect the genuine coarse whole-wheat!

Today only a handful of millers, in country places, sell stoneground whole-wheat flour—the natural flour which bakes into a rich, delicious bread such as not one in a million adults ever tasted. White bread will not give you Vitamin B, but whole-wheat bread certainly will. Nuts, peas, beans, lentils, cabbages, and sprouts are other sources of this Vitamin B group. So also are dairy products and liver and yeast.

Vitamin C is a youth-preserver, obtained best of all from *fresh* oranges, lemons, and grapefruits. If you cannot have these, try the despised turnip tops. Like potato skins, they are usually thrown away, whereas in fact they are the most nutritious part of the plant.

Whole books can and indeed have been written on the several Vitamin families. Large laboratories have been built to concoct these Vitamins artificially. *Yet the average man and woman can get all the Vitamins they need free of charge without specialized guidance.* All they need to do is to eat fresh food—fast-cooked or uncooked wherever possible—but, above all, *unprocessed food prepared for the table soon after harvesting.* Of course, this food must be eaten sensibly —by that I mean, eaten when the mind is at peace, and when there is time to chew it adequately. Remember, fresh food in preference to dried, dehydrated, canned, overcooked, long-stored food. Meals served when you have time on your hands—better no meal than a rushed meal. And, of course, proper mastication.

It is still too little realized that digestion begins immediately food passes the lips. If it is turned over to the stomach before it is fully ground down by proper mastication (during which process the digestive juices in the mouth mix with the food and prepare it for the stomach), indigestion becomes a certainty. And where there is indigestion, you may be sure that the full value of the food consumed is not being absorbed by the blood stream. Then, however much you eat, your body must remain undernourished.

Unfortunately, two thirds of the average diet consists of dead or devitalized foods. Whenever you see the expression "refined" applied to a foodstuff, you are safe in concluding that it really means *devitalized*. As explained, no food is so thoroughly devitalized as the wheat grain when "refined" into flour. Alas, a substantial portion of every meal partaken in Western countries consists of this product in one form or another—bread, pastries, puddings, etc., all completely lacking in nutriment. If, previously, you have given little thought to your meals, it is quite safe to conclude that you are already eating too much of this substance. Certainly, white flour fills you. But it doesn't fuel you.

We can leave the question of Vitamins, then, knowing that if we eat more *fresh* food in its natural state, we shall automatically ensure that we get our full Vitamin ration—and that goes for all the Vitamins, both the known and the unknown.

Better still, if you have a garden you can grow your own vegetables. Then you can be absolutely sure of maintaining a regular supply of fresh natural Vitamins—food which contains everything needful to preserve health.

In modern times we have developed "forced" crops by drugging the soil with chemicals which boost fertility—temporarily. Sooner or later the lesson of the vast dust bowls created by tree clearance and chemical farming will be learned. Then we will know that the best crops, the best Vitamins, are raised on soil which has been carefully husbanded along sensible, natural lines. Every garden-owner can meanwhile produce food far superior to taste and more loaded with Vitamins than available in the open market. He can do so without using harmful chemicals or sprays. By working with Nature instead of against her, he can grow vegetables that are better equipped to resist the ravages of pests and disease.

First, he must understand that the soil is not dead, inert matter. It is a living thing, teeming with millions of bacteria. The greater the number of bacteria, the more fertile the soil. Why?

The bacteria break down plant foods. Bacteria make the plant food available by reducing it to a state in which the plant can absorb it.

You can increase the number of bacteria in your soil by improving the physical condition of the soil so that the bacteria can multiply. And you can do it without harmful chemicals. It is achieved by manuring the ground with large quantities of partly decayed vegetable matter. This renders heavy soil more open. Water can then percolate through it easily. You thus create a light sandy soil more retentive of moisture. The bacteria work on the partly decayed vegetable matter, further breaking it down so that the plant roots can absorb even more of it. As the soil bacteria multiply, so fertility is improved.

How can you harness this powerhouse for your garden? In other words, where can you obtain sufficient quantities of partly decayed vegetable matter to add to the living soil? By building compost heaps—note the plural, *heaps*, not just one heap—and so enriching your garden through the Law of Return.

Too often what is called the compost heap is just an untidy heap of rubbish in one corner of the garden —a breeding ground for pests and an eyesore to humans. Set aside part of the garden or perhaps an adjacent piece of unused ground for creating your garden fuel. I suggest making rectangular enclosures with a few stakes and wire netting. Three such enclosures would be the ideal number. The first one should be reserved for the compost which is maturing; No. 2 for the heap which is in process of building up; and No. 3 for harder materials (such as cabbage stumps, hedge prunings, etc.) which obviously take longer to decay. The size of each enclosure should be in relation to the size of the garden or allotment—4 feet by 3 feet is about the size for a small garden plot.

The materials for composting should consist of all

vegetable waste, crop residues, lawn mowings, soft hedge trimmings, annual weeds, etc. They can be supplemented by vegetable trimmings from the kitchen, mowings and leaves from a near-by public park, leaves swept up by the road sweepers, seaweed, etc.—all such can usually be had for the labor of moving them. When none of these is obtainable, straw must be bought. It is generally quite cheap.

Of course, one could use stable or farmyard manure and have done with it. But too often these days what is called manure is nothing but straw, and the price ridiculously high.

At all times, in your home food production, you must bear in mind that your object is to *naturally* increase the number of bacteria working for you and to keep them working as long as possible. Herein, by the way, is an interesting reflection of the way Nature insists on regular rest periods. Normally, when the temperature of the soil falls in winter, the bacteria cease to be active. Then they relax! (They rest until the temperature of the soil rises again in spring).

Now, the accumulation of quantities of partially decayed vegetable matter serves a double purpose. Besides encouraging bacterial activity as rot continues, they form a dark brown spongy substance known as "humus." The presence of large quantities of humus darkens the color of the soil and increases fertility. Why?

It is well known that dark colors absorb far more of the sun's heat than do light colors. That is why we wear lighter colors in summer than in winter and why clothes worn in the tropics are always light in color.

It is an established fact that a dark soil warms up more quickly in spring than one which is light colored.

So the circle is complete:

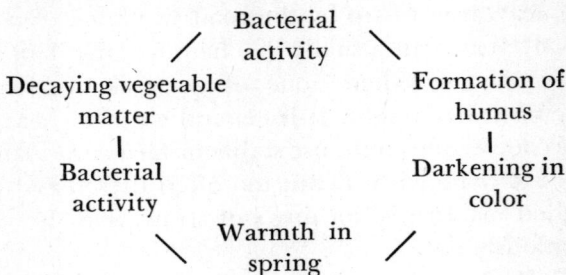

The fertility of the farm revolves around the "dunghill," as any good farmer will tell you. The fertility of the vegetable garden must likewise revolve around the compost heaps. Compost heaps, when systematically and intelligently managed, are not troublesome, and they will enable you to grow your own Vitamins.

Poultry or rabbit manure make good "activators" and only a little hydrated lime need be added. The process is very simple. Use four inches of vegetable waste, four inches of compacting a sprinkling of poultry or rabbit droppings, another four inches of compacted vegetable waste, then a sprinkling of hydrated lime. The layers should be continued in that order until the heap reaches a height of four or five feet and then allowed to mature while a second heap is being built. The time taken to mature will vary according to the season of the year and the materials used. A heap made in summer containing a high percentage of lawn mowings and lush annual weeds will mature more quickly than one made in autumn from dead leaves and the tops of herbaceous perennials. Cabbage stems and stems of brussels sprouts, soft hedge trimmings, and so on should go on to a separate heap and be given a longer period in which to become partly rotted.

A straw heap is built in exactly the same way but the straw must be well wetted before going into the heap. Old packing straw or baled straw is better than "bolten" straw as it is more broken and takes the moisture more easily. The important operation when composting straw is to get it really wet before putting it into the heap—much water is needed. When matured the finished product is almost indistinguishable from good farmyard manure, having the same ammonia smell, the same color, and the same texture.

Between April and September you should aim to keep your land constantly under crops but on the best-managed plot there are occasions when a portion of the land may be idle for a month or two. Here a green manuring crop may be grown, mustard; or if it is to stand the winter, rye. As soon as this crop is four or six inches high it should be trodden down and turned in. The bacteria will soon turn this soft young growth into rich, fertile humus.

The foregoing principles dispense with chemicals. They are based on the natural Law of Return which is the basis of all food health and of all sound husbandry. They will enable anyone owning a very small plot of land to inaugurate his own Vitamin Factory and sustain a whole family with the nearest genuine thing to "wonder food." This latter appellation, by the way, is now much used to designate dietary items thought to have special value. Don't be deceived into accepting any food as a "wonder" food and pinning all your hopes to it. Some dieticians rave about yogurt —a Bulgarian culture milk—just as, in the East, others acclaim rice as a "miracle" food. Both are, indeed, fine foods—when not spoiled by overproduction. For instance, no Eastern Yogi would think of eating the emaciated polished rice which is commercially produced in the West. *His* rice is natural rice, with the Vitamin-packed husk unremoved.

Wheat, again, might be called a "wonder" food— but not if eaten in the form of white bread with the health-giving wheat husk eliminated.

The truth is that *all* living, fresh, unprocessed foods are wonder foods, for all have something to offer you, be they vegetable, fruit, dairy produce, flesh, or fowl. Their nutriment can, however, be destroyed in preparation for the table. That is why I advise that foods which must be cooked should be cooked by the fastest means. Pressure cooking is recommended because it does the least damage.

Is there any such thing, then, as an ideal Yoga diet? No! Many Yogis are vegetarians but many, again, are not. One could hardly imagine a less vegetarian diet than freshly cooked liver. Yet this is a popular food in India—and Western dieticians confirm it to be one of the richest reservoirs of Vitamins A and B.

In this matter of food, we must resolve not to be cranks. No one can cause more irritation in a home than a food crank. If you like a vegetarian diet, by all means follow it. But do not regard yourself as thereby exalted. Or compelled to preach its virtues while others are engaged in getting their proteins from a no less natural source—*meat!*

Don't eat from habit. There are times when the appetite is "off." Respect them! They are Nature's way of warning you to go easy—so don't cram a meal because the clock says "Time for dinner." Above all, whatever you eat, be it fresh or canned, dehydrated or vitamin-loaded, don't eat it when feeling upset. In order to carry through the digestive act, your subconscious, which supervises the process, must be at peace. If you are angry, grieved, or otherwise emotionally disturbed, digestion will be incomplete.

These matters are so important, yet so often overlooked, that I repeat them. Better no meal than one eaten in a passion; or when, though in good health, you are not hungry. When the intestines are clogged and appetite vanishes, take the hint and lay off. In place of the meal you don't need, take the Deep Relaxation that you do.

Finally, once a month, as a regular routine, practice my One-Day-Fast drill. It won't hurt you, it won't interfere with your energy, and it need not stop you continuing your work. For breakfast that day, drink fresh orange juice—nothing else. For lunch, the morning and afternoon "coffee-break," and for dinner, again fresh orange juice! Only that, but as much as you like, served cold or cool or heated, as you wish. It may not sound very substantial fare but it will do

you a world of good. Everyone responds to a holiday.
Even your stomach!

This monthly One-Day-Fast may be easier to follow
on a Sunday when you are at home and can rest, but
of course the day doesn't really matter: only the importance of a regular monthly internal spring clean-
ing. When you resume eating, concentrate on a *live*
diet and you won't have to concern yourself with
Vitamins. Especially will this be so if one further
caution is observed. *Don't work your stomach to
capacity!* No factory runs its machinery at top speed
because designers always reserve a margin to prevent
unprofitable wear and tear. Apply this principle of
the margin to your feeding. Spare your stomach! Cut
down wear and tear—in other words fatigue and
exhaustion—by always rising from the table before
you are capacity-full.

These rules should not be ignored merely because
some of them now appear obvious. Review your eating habits of last week and you will be surprised how
many laws you broke. Really, your stomach is very
badly treated. It is not surprising that it should
occasionally lodge a painful protest.

Smart businessmen may dismiss my ideas because
"they take too much time." To them I say: "Sound
eating is sound economy. Because it avoids doctors'
bills, it is a good business proposition. It cuts time
lost in sickness. It keeps you fresh on the job. It
yields greater energy and fitness."

No need to study diet. Nor seek so-called (and often
expensive) "wonder" foods. No need to buy factory-
made Vitamin tablets, either. All that is required

is a little more selectivity about what you eat. And a little more time spent in masticating it.

Then you can send the dieticians packing. And leave the chemists to their business among the people whose so-called "efficient" world still has a place for them. Moreover, your long life and happiness, which you are taking steps to safeguard by other means, will be amplified.

It's so much more sensible to have *your* share of the profits on that old insurance policy, so foolish to leave it all prematurely to others.

CHAPTER 8

Modern Yogism and the Traditional Schools

I NOW invite you to pause and reflect on the ground covered. Some will say, "But much you have told us is sheer common sense." Exactly! And all the more reason for putting it into practice. Simply because a matter is straightforward and simple, do not despise it. In point of fact you are wasting your time if you do not *apply* it. That is the only way in which Yogism can be tested.

Take the Dynamic Concentration exercises. One could dress up these with much scientific mumbo jumbo, which is the fashion these days, but they would only become more complicated and less effective. The simplicity of the technique should not deceive you: master it, by attempting to carry it out for a few minutes daily, and you will be surprised at the extra control which will be acquired over the thinking processes.

Many people fail in life because of the foolish habit of mind-wandering. They flit from one thing to another, their attention held by nothing. Flotsam and jetsam they are on the waters of life—and who but themselves is accountable? It is our own defects, in the main, which hold us in check.

Others, again, so far from mind-wandering, allow their thoughts to be dominated by destructive ideas. Perhaps the cause arises first in an unsavory environment: as, for example, one wherein they are continually hearing of their shortcomings, their failures, their weaknesses, etc. If you tune in to such a chorus for any length of time, you will eventually come to believe it. Weaknesses of character which were attributed unjustly in the first place become all too real in later life. Why? Because the victim's mind automatically accepts what is being hurled at it.

Put your mind on a diet! First, don't allow it to "overeat" in the form of chaotic mental feeding as mind-wandering. Don't simply chew over this and that, without having a definite menu. Don't accept every morsel placed in front of you. Be selective.

It all turns upon this knack of concentration. Admittedly it is difficult. Some will say "I find concentration impossible." This is nonsense, for everyone concentrates. What you must do is to deepen your concentration, and begin directing it into constructive channels.

The novice will find this uncomfortable in the initial stages. But if he will carry on, doing one or two of the Dynamic Concentration exercises every day—even if he spends only five minutes on them—he will presently check the roving tendency of his thoughts and bring them under control. For the first time he will be conscious of the art of selective think-

ing. By observing his thoughts he will learn to reduce
their number during the period of the exercise.
Normally, thoughts are legion, one idea suggesting
another, and this a third, and so on endlessly. But
now, during these exercises, you can arrest this automatic multiplication. At first the effort is very hard
indeed, but it does become easier with practice. The
number of thoughts, during your exercise period,
will diminish until ultimately you are able to focus
your whole mind on just one thing.

How sweeping is the advantage gained will be
readily apparent. After all, the foundation of every
weakness of character is inability to do what one
wishes because of conflicts and distractions. Some of
these conflicts exist within oneself, but most are
external. Dynamic Concentration sorts out the conflicts, eliminates the distractions.

You are merely asked to pin your mind for brief
periods on *one* thing. It may be the tick of a watch,
the flame of a candle, or one period on a printed
page. "What a little thing"—you may say—"How can
it possibly give me more control of my *life?*" But
it is not a little thing: it is a tremendous mental feat.
It makes you stretch your mental muscles, so to speak,
in the same way as Deep Contraction calls upon your
physical muscles. It stimulates your mind in the same
way as physical exercise stimulates your body. And it
strikes at the root-cause of bad temper, intemperance,
impetuosity, etc., because these traits develop when
your thoughts are out of control. Dynamic Concentration puts your thinking processes under check.

These "simple" concentration exercises have, in

fact, a far-reaching influence. They cultivate a more serene attitude of mind in everyday life. That means less physical strain, less nervous strain. You become a more balanced individual. Outward circumstances will have less power to thwart or elate you. Your outlook will become less moody, more detached.

"But isn't life rather cold when you reach this final detachment?" On the contrary, it becomes a grander thing altogether. What a relief to be rid of tension— to look your life squarely in the face and feel the equal of whatever happens! You gain a sense of moral independence. No more scenes. No more stupid excitements. Pleasure, yes. Happiness, yes. And displeasure and unhappiness, too—but none of these need detain you long, or be felt too deeply. You will not bury yourself in the ground with sorrow, but stand up and accept it, an independent person, unhurt and undefeated.

Don't think it's a good thing to get "worked-up" to the seventh heaven when life is easy, only to plunge into abysmal despair when circumstances turn against you. That's easy and weak; in fact, it implies no action at all on your part, merely reaction to outward pressures, playing this way and that. Nor is it living. It implies existing, that's all. With a more detached and even-tempered attitude you would certainly not diminish but add to your capacity for pleasant living. And you would also prolong those happier days because there would be less tension and strain in the background, undermining your health.

There is nothing intrinsically new about my Dynamic Concentration technique. It owes much to

Yoga. The exercises suggested do not, however, seek that intensity of abstraction which all the historic Yoga systems advocate. Traditionally, the student was first taught *Pratyahara*. This means withdrawing the mind from all save a single thought. As you now know, that isn't easy. But it is not impossible: it can be done!

Our object in Yogism is to turn this art of focus to constructive ends, so that we become abler, finer citizens. The Yogi's object struck much deeper. It was his first step along the road to God-union.

From *Pratyahara* he passed to the state of *Dharana*, wherein the art of concentration becomes perfect. But already, at this stage, we have parted company with him—we to carry on with our everyday tasks; he, to seek a new world of mysticism. On goes the Yogi, practicing strange disciplines to make him still more adept at mental abstraction. Soon he has advanced beyond the deepest form of concentration. He has reached the stage known as *Dhyana*—a state of intense meditation. Now he is temporarily out of touch with the physical world; but still he is dissatisfied. *Samadhi* beckons: he must deepen his meditation still further—until at last he becomes conscious of one thing and one thing only: perfect absorption into God.

Naturally, concentration of this kind requires years of intense practice. It is divorced completely from everyday modern life. How far Western advocates of traditional Yoga can advance toward it remains highly speculative. I, personally, do not believe they can proceed very far. Indeed, what traditional Yoga asks of its disciples would stagger the well-meaning persons whose loose translations of stray Sanskrit texts are so frequently served up as "authentic" Yoga. Lest any reader of this book be deceived by them, I would point out that traditional Yoga insists upon regular fasting, nonactivity, silence, independence of any set routine, resistance to weakness of every kind, and, above all, avoidance of others' society. This hermit-like existence may be good for the soul, but it would conflict with present-day responsibilities and would certainly be impossible in a civilized environment. It would involve removing from your life all feminine (or masculine) society; all comforts such as beds, seats, and clothing; all pleasures such as dainty dishes, music, ornaments; all possessions such as gold, silver, copper, gems, wood; all entertainments such as dancing. It would mean depriving yourself of wife (or husband) and children. It would mean transport on foot and not by car. It would mean divesting yourself of all power and authority. And what I have just elaborated are merely a few of the minimum impediments to Yoga listed in the *Siva Samhita* and the *Hatha Yoga Pradipika*—classical authorities on authentic Yoga.

Let there be no doubt that the genuine Yogi's recoil from worldly associations must be complete and absolute. In addition, he must observe the ten *Yamas* or commandments: Never to cause injury to another, never to steal, never to be guilty of incontinence; but always to speak the truth, be ready to forgive, show compassion, be sincere, eat little, and keep a state of great cleanliness externally and internally (the latter by washing the intestines in accordance with a complicated exercise of Hatha Yoga).

Where, then, you find the claim that this or that is genuine, authentic Yoga, the foregoing standards should be looked for—irrespective of which of the many systems of Yoga is named. Those who set up as *Gurus* or teachers will, if authentic, leave you in no doubt of their exceptional purity. Their day will begin long before dawn, when they rise in their simple, primitive dwelling to enter the blessed state of *Samadhi;* in which condition of abstraction they will continue for many hours.

Anyone attempting to study genuine Yoga must therefore do so with his eyes open; for alas, false teachers are numerous and only too ready to impose upon the uninitiated. I believe it impossible to practice traditional Yoga under civilized conditions, and that the claim to have done so is either mistaken or pretended. Here we are, living in the twentieth century, in modern houses, with modern creature comforts, modern obligations, and modern services. Don't let us pretend what we are not, or condemn out of hand the age and environment whose fruits we enjoy. For all its imperfections, civilization has *some* good points. It may encourage us to lead a narrow, unhealthy life, but we can avoid that if we will and, still enjoying civilized benefits, retain our health and increase our years by sensible attitudes and exercises. Genuine Yoga has unquestionably a contribution to make. But our very upbringing and surroundings make it impossible for a Westerner to absorb it whole.

There must be a compromise, whatever branch of Yoga is chosen.

In the Yogism system I have tried to make this compromise easy for Western people. The fantastic aspects of the traditional Yogas are rejected. The adaptation is avowedly and intentionally for every-day civilized life. The subtleties of early Sanskrit texts are left to the handful of modern scholars who possess the technical equipment to understand them. We are concerned with practical advantages, such as may be obtained without entirely disrupting life.

Withdrawal to a lonely mountain retreat may be necessary for the practice of *Samadhi,* but it is out of reach to twentieth-century people. Yet who will deny the value of a few minutes spent daily in Deep Relaxation in one's own home? I go further and say that any person who will devote a whole hour a week to this exercise will become, in the course of a few months, a healthier, abler person in every way. For this small inconvenience, he will be repaid a thousandfold. Nor need he trouble himself with Yogic abstractions. Mystical experiences need not enter into it—indeed, if he is to continue to live a normal life, they had better not. But an hour a week, spent in your own room, away from other members of the family—such an hour of complete physical and mental rest will rejuvenate your body and soothe your nervous system in a way nothing else can do. Some discreet organizing may be necessary to create the conditions and the opportunity, in the average home, but if you make the experiment a few times, you will need no encouragement to continue further.

So far I have presented the four basic Yogism exercises in isolated forms. In reality, they are closely integrated. A truly dynamic state of concentration cannot be achieved without mastering the art of relaxation. Likewise, it is impossible to carry out Deep Relaxation without bending thought dynamically on the particular stretch involved. The four basic Yogism exercises supplement each other. Their practice will make and keep your mind and body young.

CHAPTER 9

Theories and Practices of Traditional Yoga

HOWEVER impossible it may be to practice authentic Yoga in the twentieth century—and I think I have said enough to show it really *is* impossible—one may still enjoy a glimpse of the ocean of speculation embodied in it.

These early Yogis who lived such austere, indrawn lives—what did they believe? I have said they were the forerunners of modern psychology. Can this be proved?

A hundred years ago little, if anything, was known in the West about psychology. Other branches of scientific inquiry had certainly taken shape. But psychology was late arriving. A century ago the very word *psychology* had only begun to circulate.

That civilized man came so late to the scene of mental discovery is in itself a significant fact. He was slow to study his own mind because his nature was materialistic. Other, more "solid" interests monopolized his attention. Industry, invention, speed—things like these captured and helped his fancy. And he became very good at them—so proficient that today he knows more, much more about the workings of his watch than of his brain. True, this lack of interest in his own personality is slowly being remedied. Civilized man knows how to organize, whatever else he does not know. Once he conceived the idea of investigating his inner mental world, he accordingly set about it in characteristic fashion. He dissected the organs of the brain, hoping to trap the forces that worked it. He invented machines to chart mental reactions. He conducted all manner of "controlled" experiments. And, as you might expect, he formed a galaxy of theory to explain everything neatly and systematically. Fresh experiments led to fresh theories, however, and today the whole field of mental research is alive with conflicting conjecture. Feeling between the various schools of psychology is often quite intense—and the new science, which arrived so late, seems destined to remain a battlefield for decades to come.

Though this notion of self-exploration is new to modern man, it was certainly not novel to the ancients. For thousands of years exponents of Yoga have preoccupied themselves with it. Coming, as it does, across the span of centuries, their phraseology may sound obscure and quaint to our ears, but the substance is arresting.

Though they lived long before scientific methods were evolved, they outdistanced us both in the sweep and in the intensity of their investigations. Yet to say so is no discredit to present-day psychological inquiry. Though materialistic in form, it is filling gaps which the Yogis by-passed in their desire to press on to the root of the matter.

One of the greatest of the Yoga psychologists was Patanjali. Just who he was and when exactly he lived remains a mystery. But historians are agreed that he put together, in his famous *Sutras*, the best syntheses of Yoga that have yet been compiled. What he did was to edit ideas current for hundreds of years, condensing this wealth of material into a highly selective digest. This digest, called the *Yoga Sutras*, is available in several translations, but I warn the reader that, though a key source of Yoga theory, its study means very hard going.

Remember that Patanjali was writing for contemporaries, not posterity. Moreover, he was writing for people who were already treading the Yoga path, not novices. With brilliant economy, therefore, he could afford to telescope whole chapters into sentences, whole paragraphs into words. That is why, although the complete *Sutras* occupy less than ten pages of large type, they set forth an elaborate outline of psychology and philosophy.

Patanjali did not concern himself with persuading or special pleading. Statements are given "cold"—not argued. Their author knew that his followers needed no convincing. All they asked was a comprehensive theory into which they could fit facts verified by personal experience. Patanjali gave them this.

In the West we have become accustomed to associate meditation with mystics and monks. Patanjali had no such illusion. He advised every man to practice it as a first step to self-understanding. "What more natural than to study the mind by such inner observation?" he seemed to ask. Yet before one can begin to understand the mind, one must discipline and train the mind in the technique of understanding. Hence the great amount of introspective analysis that accompanies all traditional Yoga teaching, that of Patanjali being no exception.

Our modern scientific instinct would be to dismiss these meditative practices as hocus-pocus. But with equal right the Yogi might reject our own scientific devices and unimaginative statistics. He could dismiss them because they only scratch the surface. He could say that their results were, in any case, unreliable—being subject to interpretation by minds untrained in separating reality from illusion.

Here, then, at the very commencement of our examination we come to the parting of the ways: here is the difference between the modern and the ancient approach. The Yogi launched boldly forth on a tidal wave of inward analysis; the modern scientist wades discreetly near the shore, concerned that no wave of "emotionalism" shall submerge him.

Patanjali defined Yoga as a means of steadying and controlling thought and feeling. How otherwise, he implied, can we distinguish between the true and the false? Thus the *Sutras* strike deep in this, their very first sentence. We see at once the distance that divides them from modern psychological methods.

When the *chitta* or "mind-stuff" has been steadied and controlled—when, in other words, our concentration has been awakened so that we can really direct our thoughts—then the mind exists in "unmodified form." Mercurial thought is checked. Fleeting emotions are trapped. The individual becomes, for the first time, conscious of Self.

In normal life the Self is submerged in a wholly illusory and ephemeral world. False ideas are accepted concerning time, reality and so forth. Normally, too, we are conscious of Self simply by what we imagine we see, hear, touch, etc. In other words, we allow outward phenomena to come between us and our true self. We fail to take a detached, independent view: rather, what we think is something that is *imposed* upon us, all the time, from without.

And what we know about ourselves arises from these confused and distorted sensory impressions. Is it any wonder, then, that we know so little about human personality, having regard to our chaotic mental state?

Patanjali lists five types of mental function—some painful, some pleasant. These functions, he says, are Knowledge, Confusion, Delusion, Sleep, and Memory. They, and only they, are the tools we use to fashion our picture of life.

Let us examine these tools. Knowledge is derived from clear perception and inference. Confusion arises from our inability to distinguish between a true and a false picture—*e.g.,* seeing a thing in a form which is contrary to its real nature. Delusion arises from mistaking words for reality (modern philosophers, please note!). As for Sleep, we can all agree that it curtails external perception; and Memory is an accurate recollection of the past.

Patanjali then warns us to examine our mental activity more critically—to be on our guard against mistaking fancy for knowledge, illusion for reality. Having so warned us, he goes on to indicate the means by which such discrimination may be made.

Control of the mind is the key. This control is acquired by disciplining thought and cultivating a detached attitude. How to discipline thought? By concentration. How to become detached? By ceasing to immerse one's Self in the external, fleeting, illusory world of the senses.

Naturally, such mental discipline and detachment are possible only through persistent endeavor. Unruly habits of thought cannot be checked by unsystematic, irregular effort. We must be very much in earnest, continuously and tirelessly restraining mental impressions. Initially this restraint will be highly exhausting and discouraging. But the final reward—a clear, steady mind—certainly justifies the effort.

Every stage in Patanjali's wonderful treatise represents not a single step forward, but a bounding leap. Non-attachment, for instance, which he indicates as the next stage, involves a tremendous achievement. It means more, much more, than merely detaching one's concept of Self from the picture of life formulated by mere sense perceptions. It means more, much more, than mere "withdrawing." It means completely dissociating one's Self from the fruits of action. It means an act of complete Renunciation. To the West it might be more comprehensible, perhaps, by recalling the words of Christ—"Except ye become as little children, ye cannot enter the Kingdom of Heaven."

Until now these deathless words have, perhaps, implied merely simple innocence to Western readers. But Yoga bids us look a lot more deeply into them, if we would enjoy this higher life.

To begin with, nonattachment is bound to be spasmodic. With practice it can become a steady state. The mind is then no longer at the mercy of the senses. *Samadhi* has been reached.

No one can reach *Samadhi* by mere negative introspection. Only a discriminating, energetic approach makes it possible. Spiritual devotions help, of course. Patanjali says that devotion to God is one of the swiftest routes—devotion which takes the form of contemplation upon the idea of God; all that He stands for and implies.

Already certain "obstacles" will have reared their ugly heads, discouraging advancement. These "obstacles" are ill health, boredom, skepticism, carelessness, sloth, materialism, ignorance, sidetracking, and lack of perseverance. Unpleasant experiences can also discourage headway. To avoid such unpleasant and disturbing experiences and to assist in overcoming the "obstacles," the student must practice special breathing and concentration exercises. He must also foster a generous and tolerant attitude to others. Above all he must pass through the gateway of meditation—meditation on the saints, meditation on God —for this meditation is the greatest of all means of controlling mental activity. When the mind is thus controlled, it is capable of reflecting truly, like a pure crystal, everything that is seen.

Patanjali discourses on the various types of meditation, of which the highest form is "complete absorption"—a state where there is nothing more to discriminate between, so that the mind becomes perfectly poised.

This brings us to the end of the first part of the *Sutras*. The second part is more technical, containing specific instructions on the various Yoga exercises. Again the opening passage cuts adrift from contemporary psychological methods. One must pursue an austere life, dedicating oneself to Divine Service, says Patanjali. The number of Western psychologists who begin their studies with this preparation must be few! Patanjali's object now is to rid the seeker of five impediments to further advancement: (1) Ignorance, (2) Pride, (3) Desire, (4) Aversion, and (5) Fear.

Of these five obstacles, Ignorance is regarded as the greatest. Most people's thought is dominated by these "obstacles." Their ignorance is due to mistaking appearance for reality. Pride comes from identifying their Selves, and consequently their concept of life, with the misleading impressions of the five senses and, indeed, with these misleading senses themselves. Desire arises from attaching importance to pleasure. Aversion is the normal, instinctive recoil from anything that is unpleasant or painful. Fear is the dread of the unknown, fundamentally caused by the terror of death.

The method whereby these motivations become outlawed is Concentration. By training the mind to fix intently upon one thing, it is possible to divest oneself of all impediments, says Patanjali. And now he brings us to a concept immediately abhorrent to

Western peoples—the idea of *Karma* and Rebirth. Not until one has freed oneself from these five impediments, declares Patanjali, can the Self break free from the wheel of rebirth. So long as these obstacles remain, so long is the Self predestined to experience again and again the tribulations of rebirth.

Karma (which is the natural consequences of past actions) is unavoidable. But by carefully avoiding fresh ignorance, illusion, desire, and so forth, the Self can start creating *Karma* of a new kind. In attempting to create this new *Karma*, the Self will become conscious of its separateness from, and independence of, the fleeting, everyday, transitory phenomena of life. These happenings, hitherto looked upon as real and independent, are discovered to be only the projections of a confused mind.

Thus by renunciation, by diligently separating cause from effect, by clearly discriminating between false and true, the adept at length achieves liberation. Certain sacred vows have to be taken—and observed in minute detail and on every occasion: nonviolence, complete honesty, perfect continence, desirelessness, and nontheft. When the Yogi has eliminated all violence from thought and action, enmity ceases. With complete honesty, truth shines. With perfect continence, he acquires greater energy. When desirelessness is developed, life becomes plain and clear for the first time. The Yogi's attitude is now supremely cheerful, concentrated, self-assured, and *content*. Through denial he has rid his mind of impurity and replaced the old illusions with bright new spiritual perceptions. Through devotion, he has come to know

God. Through *asanas* (or postures) and *Pranayama* (breathing exercises), he has steadied the nervous system. Through relaxation, he has deepened his quality of meditation. And through meditation he has completely subjugated the senses.

Now, in Part Three of the *Sutras,* we are given instruction on the actual technique of meditation. First of all, *Dharana*—fixing the attention on any one object; which practice, when perfected, gives the mind the ability to achieve *Dhyana* (or union with the chosen object). The mind then becomes completely absorbed in the object. No fleeting thought, no passing emotion, can now disturb the calm surface of thought. *Samadhi* is the final stage—wherein this mystic concentration becomes so perfect that union, as such, is surpassed—only the object itself now exists.

This explains why devotees of Yoga sit for days in a detached, metaphysical state, completely oblivious to the material world, entirely absorbed and serene. They have reached *Samadhi*. But they have not reached it overnight. It requires years of self-denial, and regularity in performing complicated breathing and physical exercises designed to control all "normal" bodily and mental sensation. Once *Samadhi* is reached, the mind can appreciate knowledge direct. Previously, such knowledge was impossible. Now, however, past and future are merged; finite and infinite have become one; all manner of psychic powers have been developed. Nor is the liberated Yogi's knowledge limited to this planet: his enlightenment is so complete that nothing in the Universe is beyond him. He can, in spirit, leave his body for long periods. The body will subsist without food. It will be unaffected by germs, heat, or cold.

In the fourth and last part of the *Sutras* Patanjali discusses the Self that controls the mental functions. This Self is not to be confused with the mental mechanism. In fact, Patanjali's philosophy is trinitarian: it postulates (1) a Self; (2) a Mind, and (3) a Physical World, all three being separate and existing apart. In these final passages we are asked to study the relationship between the three. We soon realize that this Self-awareness, toward which the earlier *Sutras* have been moving, is an exalted and all-powerful state, quite removed from the Western "goody-goody" concept of spirituality. Patanjali says the Yogi learns to forge new lives, for his Self: he develops new minds, new bodies, through rebirth. And Memory—one of the basic tools, remember?—is pushed back beyond the limits of a single life to recall preceding incarnations, so that the Yogi ultimately conceives the sum of all his lives and knows the goal toward which his subliminal Self is advancing. Actions separated by time, and country, as he has moved from life to life, become part of a coordinated pattern—actions which were taken through former bodies and former minds! Past, present, and future merge into one. "There is nothing which Self does not know." And this Self—this deathless eternal essential You—goes on, always distinct from the mind, from the bodies, and from the external phenomena in which it was formerly "lost." Thus the Self passes from life to life, purifying itself in the process, until all that is tainted, illusory, and false ceases to be, and sublime fulfilment is reached for ever.

The foregoing sketchy outline of the *Sutras* will indicate the broad general lines along which Yoga metaphysics proceeds. It should not be thought, however, that instruction is lacking to dot the *i*'s and cross the *t*'s. For example, Bhoja's commentary on the *Sutras* lists five states of mind—dispersion, confusion, imperfect stability, concentration, absorption. There are "Eight Principal Attainments" which read like a page from Hans Andersen. They are *Anima*—the ability to become small as an atom; *Mahima,* the ability to increase size; *Laghima,* the ability to diminish bodily weight; *Garima,* the ability to increase weight; *Prapti,* the ability to transport oneself through space; *Prakayama,* the ability to materialize one's thoughts; *Vashitva,* the ability to control nature; and *Ishitva,* the ability to rule all things.

It seems to me that Sanskrit scholars and others make a mistake when they interpret these "attainments" so literally. They were not intended to be regarded as physical realities; rather, as feats of the mind. "To become small as an atom"—surely, the capacity to concentrate on the infinitely little?" "To be transported through space"—surely, by extrasensory perception (a phenomenon now scientifically verified), not physically as on the magic carpet of desire.

This also applies to the "Thirty Subsidiary Attainments," which include feats like rendering oneself invisible (surely not fairylike, but by extreme meekness of spirit, etc.). But no such rationalizing will

account for the "Six Purification Acts" which all
authentic Yogis must undertake. One of these acts
is the cleansing of the bowels—first, by drawing air
into the intestines and forcibly expelling it; second,
by drawing in and then expelling water. Such practices are clearly dangerous and difficult. Stomach-
cleansing, another of the Purification Acts, is likewise
beyond the average Western student's control. It
involves swallowing a cloth over 250 inches long and
subsequently regurgitating it. (The nose is similarly
cleansed by means of a string of ten or more strands.)
Purification Acts which go to these extreme lengths
are not to be attempted lightly. Western medicine
would have much to say about the needs for hygienic
instruments. Once again, however, we are reminded
of how seriously and earnestly Yogis take to their
subject, and how foolish it is for modern men to
claim to emulate them.

For the record, then, here is a list of twenty basic
Asanas or postures. I reproduce the descriptions of
the first seventeen from a famous source book on
Hatha Yoga—the *Gheranda Samhita,* which adheres,
sometimes verbatim, to the other great expositor of
Hatha Yoga—*Hatha Yoga Pradipika*. The translation
from the Sanskrit was done by Sri Chandra Vasu and
published in Madras in 1933.

However, I warn the student that he will find many
discrepancies among the descriptions of these ancient
Yogic *asanas*. Sanskrit sources give only fragmentary
accounts, whereas some of the more complex postures
obviously require lengthy description. Hence, no
doubt, the disparities which have crept in; but they

need not embarrass the student of Yogism, as the regular practice of Deep Contraction obviates the necessity of assuming more difficult postures. Many of the historic poses are quite unsuited to Western use. The list below is given solely for its historic interest:

The practitioner who has subdued his passions, having placed one heel at the anal aperture should keep the other heel on the root of the generative organ; afterward he should rest his chin upon the chest, and being quiet and straight, gaze at the spot between the two eyebrows.

1. *Siddhasana*

Place the right foot on the left thigh and similarly the left one on the right thigh, also cross the hands behind the back and firmly catch hold of the great toes of feet so crossed. Place the chin on the chest and fix the gaze on the tip of the nose.

2. *Padmasana*

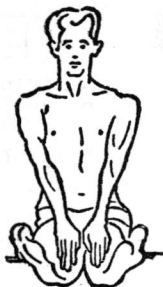

Make the thighs tight like vajra and place the legs by the two sides of the anus.

3. *Vajrayudhasana*

The two heels to be placed under the scrotum contrariwise (*i.e.*, left heel on the right side and the right heel on the left side of it) and turned upward, the knees to be placed on the ground, and the hands placed on the knees, mouth to be kept open; practicing the *Jalandhara mudra* one should fix his gaze on the tip of the nose.

4. *Simhasana*

One leg (the right foot) to be placed on the other (left) thigh, and the other foot to be turned backward.

5. *Virasana*

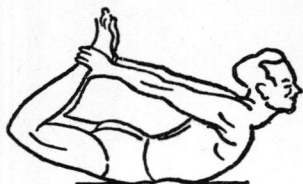

Stretch the legs on the ground like a stick, and catch hold of (the toes of) the feet with the hands, making the body like a bow.

6. *Dhanurasana*

Lying flat on the ground (on one's back) like a corpse is called the *Mrtasana* (the Corpse posture).

7. *Mrtasana*

Make the *Padmasana* (2) posture without the crossing of the arms; lie on the back, holding the head by the two elbows.

8. *Matsyasana*

Stretch the two legs on the ground, stiff like a stick (the heels not touching), and place the forehead on the two knees, and catch with the hands the toes.

9. *Pascimottanasana*

Placing the left foot and the leg on the ground, surround the left foot by the right leg; and place the two hands on the two knees.

10. *Samkatasana*

Place the palms of the two hands on the ground, place the umbilical region on the two elbows, stand upon the hands, the legs being raised in the air, and crossed like *Padmasana* (2).

11. *Mayurasana*

Sitting on the ground, cross the legs in the *Padmasana* (2) posture, thrust down the hands between the thighs and the knees, stand on the hands, supporting the body on the elbows.

12. *Kukkutasana*

Assume the Cock (12) posture, catch
hold of the neck with the hands, and
stand stretched like a tortoise.

13. *Uttanakurmakasana*

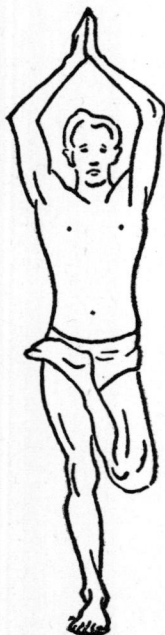

Stand straight on one leg (the right), bending
the left leg, and placing the left foot on
the root of the right thigh; standing thus like
a tree on the ground.

14. *Vrksasana*

Lie on the ground
face downward, the
two hands being
placed on the chest,
touching the ground
with the palms,
raise the legs in the
air 18 inches high.

15. *Salabhasana*

Let the body, from
the navel down-
ward to the toes,
touch the ground,
place the palms on
the ground, raise
the head (the upper
portion of the body)
like a serpent.

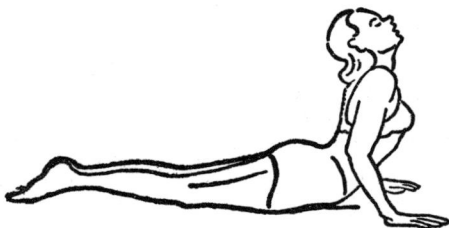

16. *Bhujangasana*

Turn the feet upward, place
them on the knees; then place
the hands on the ground with
the palms turned upward; inspire, and fix the gaze on the tip
of the nose.

17. *Yogasana*

The following additional postures are also commonly used:

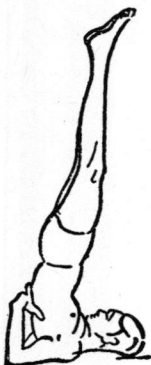

Lie on your back, then raise the legs slowly together until they are pointing vertically upward and you are balanced on your shoulders. Place the hands on the hips and use them as support, as you raise your legs.

18. *Sarvangasana*

Lie on your back, then raise the legs slowly together and carry them over until the toes touch the ground above your head. Palms flat on the ground throughout.

19. *Halasana*

Kneel on the ground. Bend forward and place your forearms on the ground at right angles to each other, with fingers interlocked. Place your head in your palms and raise the legs slowly until you are balanced vertically on your head.

20. *Sirsasana*

You, as a Western student, need not look wistfully at the foregoing list and the accompanying sketches, bemoaning the fact that you have neither the time nor the physique to master such complicated exercises. They are not necessarily the Open Sesame to Hidden Knowledge. They are merely the ritual of Hatha Yoga, which is the kindergarten school of all traditional Yoga systems. My friend, Dr. Paul Brunton, who has written the best English books on traditional Yoga— books to which I refer you for further illumination on that subject—spent many years traveling off the beaten track in India meeting exponents of Yoga in all its manifold forms. Today he pursues his studies in the United States; for he now knows Yoga can be studied anywhere and these complicated physical gymnastics represent only a phase of the subject.

Because you have a job to do, a family to support, civic responsibilities to shoulder, you are not thereby debarred from the study or adaptation of Yoga. Far from it. Your need of Yogic help is the more pronounced. If your motives are good, if you approach the subject in humility and sincerity, physical handicaps matter not at all. Wherever you live, whatever your physique, if your objects are good, your progress will be greater than that of Indian students animated only by self-glorification.

Yoga in the East has too often been exploited as a short cut to fairyland. Lots of Indian Yogis seek to master these *asanas* not to achieve spiritual development but to display their muscular powers. If your object is not self but Understanding, then to that extent you are better placed than they to make the most of this study.

Of course, this adaptation of Yoga will help you in other ways for which the Indian has little need. It will help you to accept the stress and strain of civilized living. It will enable you to adjust yourself to the trials of modern life. Some people find this help through prayer. Others seek it through an artistic hobby or by making music or by creating a garden.

Such things certainly enhance peace of mind, which is the one boon above all others which our mad, distracted world needs. But alas, not all men can find abiding satisfaction from these pursuits. Mostly the peace that is gained is only fleeting and partial.

That is why Yogism can even mean more to you than traditional Yoga means to those who live in the East. Because of your greater physical distractions, you are better placed to value it. For example, the fact that you lead a hectic life in the city enables you to realize the full importance of relaxation.

None of us is so wholly occupied every day as to be unable to find a few minutes for the basic Yogism exercises. They do not call for gymnastic skill. No man or woman is so busy or important as to be unable to reserve a little time for concentration exercises.

You live in an apartment? You have no room of your own? But are there no parks, no fields, no churches? Believe me, once you learn the Yogism methods of relaxation and concentration, you will create the opportunities to indulge them, for they will bring light into your life.

Deep Relaxation you must learn to restore your flagging energies, soothe your worn nerves. Dynamic Concentration you must develop to endow an otherwise meaningless life with significance and purpose. And the postures listed above will not greatly worry you if you study their adaptation in the form of Deep Contractions.

In your hands you possess terrible powers. You have the power to make yourself healthier and happier. The power to diminish your difficulties. The power to influence others this way also. Yes, and you have, too, the power to make your lot worse than it need be, to make your health and happiness only fitful. You have the power to make your burdens heavier, to spread abroad the seeds of despair and frustration.

Use these great powers discreetly—for your own sake, for the sake of your family, your friends. Modern Yogism teaches you how. It will teach you surely, though you live in Brooklyn and not the Himalayas. In fact, there is more need for Yoga in the Brooklyns of this world than in its silent, lonely places.

Yoga, then, is not the preserve of any group of Indian ascetics. It is for Everyman ... everywhere. And that means *you*.

CHAPTER 10

Yogism and Long Life

SCIENTISTS are still hoping for a serum that will prolong life to the span of a hundred years or more. Though such an elixir has fascinated mankind throughout the ages, I doubt if our century will be any more successful in discovering it. Aging is a natural process. It cannot be stopped. Retarded it may be, but not stopped. Hastened, too, it can be, as we know to our loss.

For example, it is natural for the artery walls to harden with advancing years. But the pace at which they harden can be reduced. Properly oxygenated blood is one way, *e.g.*, the practice of Dynamic Breathing. Proper exercise is another, *e.g.*, Deep Contraction. Again, cell growth throughout the body diminishes with advancing years. Never relax, and it will diminish faster. Air, relaxation, and exercise have therefore much to do with this natural process of aging. Dynamic Breathing, Deep Relaxation, and Deep Contractions are manifestly helpful in prolonging our days. And as the harmony of body and mind can be upset by destructive thinking, clearly Dynamic Concentration is another life-preserver.

It is through such methods as these—drugless, natural methods—that I look for the further expansion of life. We must get clear in our minds the idea that health is a natural condition of man, disease unnatural. And that old age and good health are not necessarily incompatible.

Why, then, has a youth eighteen years old, 50 per cent less chance of surviving than one who is ten? And why does this ratio become worse with advancing years? Because nature sends us forth well protected for life's journey, and as we grow older we wear down the protective "skin." It is when the defenses pass under our own direct control that we begin to take liberties and run risks—and all this must be paid for.

Even though survival prospects are higher for younger people, many civilized countries now face a period of declining numbers of young people and a higher population of old people. This paradox comes about through the drop in the birth rate and the increase in life expectancy. It is one of the big problems of the future. It presents real dangers to civilization unless our aging populations take steps to renew their hold on life.

Most people approaching seventy have become converted to the idea that in some way they are ill, must be ill, and cannot help being ill. They have come to believe that health for them is unnatural, ill health to be expected. They have also hypnotized themselves into thinking that life is almost over for them at seventy. These subconscious notions vitally affect the health of the elderly and it is urgent that we dispel them. We have also to rid our minds of the

notion that retirement must take place at a certain
age. I am quite sure most people would live longer
if they ceased thinking that health was something
beyond them. Somehow, we must destroy this mental
picture of old age implying illness and decrepitude.
It need be neither if we use our minds and bodies
intelligently.

Imagine this future world dominated by a growing
percentage of old people. What kind of society will
there be, if they continue to be absorbed in their
complaints, convinced they are dying anyhow, and
should be retired? Medical science must strive to
show that these assumptions, however widely held,
are baseless. In fact, old people are better protected
against many complaints than young folk—certainly,
if they have learned sense. They are also wiser and
more economical in their actions. They have experience, which no excess of spirits can supply. As regards
aging, this is only the continuance of something which
began the day they were born and is never ending.
People don't start to age suddenly. There is nothing
more unnatural about aging at eighty than at eight,
except that at eighty you should know better how to
take care of yourself. Gladstone was Prime Minister
of England at eighty-three, but if he had retired from
politics, and ceased to lead an active life, he would
probably have died ten years younger. An active man
at eighty is less likely to be under sentence of death
than an inactive one of forty.

Of course, the older you grow, the more you need
to slow up the feverish tempo at which inexperienced
young people live. In fact, the sooner you strike this

equilibrium, the easier will it be to reach your century! Most motorists give more attention to the engines of their cars than they give to their own wonderful bodies. If we had service stations for humans, we would see they were properly decarbonized by Deep Relaxation and properly fueled by Dynamic Breathing. We would realize that air is as important to the driver as to his tires.

We would discover, too, that it is possible to carry too heavy a load, and it is possible to drive too long in top gear. Neither of these things is good for an automobile and neither is good for the driver. If he travels each day with a great load of tension and worry, something is bound to give, sooner or later (probably his digestion). If he drives himself always in top gear, he is bound to encounter trouble one day. His health—by that we mean the sweet running of his personal mechanism—is as responsive to these strains as the cruder mechanism of his automobile. Again, there are times when one can coast downhill. There are times when overheating occurs, and a rest is advisable. Strange that we should study and accept these conditions when driving a vehicle that costs only a few hundred dollars, yet ignore them in regard to life, which is priceless.

The century mark is a realizable target for man if he decides to live with, instead of continually running against, the Highway Code of Nature. An eagle can live to be a hundred years old, and innumerable human beings have proved they can perform the same feat. One scientific theory (developed by Bogomolet) is that total life can be *at least* five times the period of growth. On this minimum basis, if a man can live until seventy-five, with decent precautions a hundred years is equally attainable. The remarkable fact is not that few civilized men live to be a hundred. Considering how we occupy ourselves, it is amazing that so many of us live half as long as we do!

It is worth studying, this business of prolonging life. To give five minutes a day to relaxation, five minutes to contraction, five minutes to breathing, and five minutes to thinking is to ask *in toto* only twenty minutes of your time. In return for this you can perhaps add another twenty or twenty-five years to your life—and make all the years in between more congenial!

Alas, many will dismiss this as impossible. They will get up tomorrow as usual, gulp down a cup of boiling coffee, rush to work, sit in a stuffy office or factory for hours without exercise, eat indigestible meals, and find relief from tension in alcoholic stimulants. They will entirely forget about relaxing. If nature allowed them, they would also forget about breathing. True, they will imbibe something from the atmosphere by unconscious respiration—just enough to keep ticking over. They will grow stiff and constipated by inadequate exercise, and they will worry their heads off by reflex thinking. And these very folk will condemn the Yogis as fanatics—could anything be more fanatical than their own situation?

Such people—men and women who never have a moment's real relaxation—are deciding the fate of the world. For it is these prematurely old people who hold the seats of government, who decide what industry shall do, whether war will take place. They are the people who wield authority and power. In their hands is the fate of humanity.

We should ask them—How, if a man so despises the laws of natural living that he gives them no place in his own life, can he make wise decisions for his fellows? If he pictures his own life as almost over and done with, how can he lay down the future for others? If he is ill from his own unnatural living, how can he bestow well-being on his followers?

It is urgent that we develop an altogether new attitude to this business of growing old. Our present outlook is fearfully wrong. In the older society into which we are moving, we must come to terms with the process of aging. We have got to accept it as natural but *flexible*. We must do what we can to delay it. Above all, we must realize that men can live and *enjoy* life at ninety—enjoy it with more relish, and with greater usefulness, than when they were nine.

Finally, we have got to get rid of that shocking fallacy that old people are necessarily a burden to their families. Make an elderly person feel he is a nuisance, that there is nothing more for him to do, and you go a long way toward killing him off.

One day we shall discover that not many people die of old age. And not many old people die of sickness. They die because they have lost interest in life. They die because they are not wanted. They die because they are idle, and have nothing to do. Very often, they die because of the feeling that life has already passed them by. But most of all they die for their own sins—

tension, anxiety, and the like. Germs have little hand in it. Attitudes are far more important.

The heart of many an elderly person who has died has been as strong as an ox. But it was broken.

CHAPTER 11

Approaching the End of the Road

RETURNING to the objectives with which we set forth, little doubt remains that the early Yogis were intensely interested in this question of long life and happiness. Admittedly, their methods are out of tune with present day needs. Yet we can learn from them, even if it means modifying what we learn. Though we cannot apply strictly traditional Yoga, we can still make use of its findings.

In Yogism we have done just that. But why, you may ask, all this insistence on longer living? It is not that I personally have an "old-age" complex. It is rather that this question must be faced by every civilized country. On the one hand we have a declining birth rate: fewer young people are coming along. On the other, we have a higher number of old people, both relatively and actually. For with fewer births the ratio of old people is automatically increased. And with better medical care, which most civilized countries now possess, life expectation is sure to increase.

Look, then, at this brave *old* world so rapidly advancing upon us.

In 1900, according to figures published by the U.S. Bureau of the Census, 1 in every 25 people in the United States was aged 65 or more; in 1950, the figure was already 1 in 12 people. By 1975, so the U.S. Department of Labor calculates, *the figure will be about 1 in 7.*

Eventually we shall get down to this problem, of course. But already it is urgent. Yogism can help us face it. Add to medical skill its quota of psychological stimulus—use of the four-way formula (Concentration, Breathing, Contraction, and Relaxation). This can, indeed, make people much happier, if only by relieving the tensions which undermine their health. Then they can look forward with reasonable certainty to living longer and, what is equally important, enjoying that longer life as healthy and active persons.

Why does not civilization face these psychological factors now—factors which directly influence human life—in the same practical way that it handles industrial problems? Undoubtedly because of the hard core of materialism at its center. No industry would think of using metals without first investigating the tensions, stresses, and strains those metals could withstand. Why, then, this indifference to *human* strains?

We need a metallurgy of the mind. I submit that in Yogism we have at least the outline of such a system. But what a commentary on civilized values that metals (which are reasonably straightforward conglomerations of atoms anyway), receive so much more

attention than human minds, which are a seething
mass of complications! I don't know how many millions are spent annually on metallurgy: I do know
that precious little is spent on analyzing human
tensions.

Fortunately, the way to relieve human tension is
reasonably simple. Most of the difficulty lies in making people aware of the power of personal adjust-
ment. Once they are conscious of their ability to
diminish the strains they suffer, they are well on the
way to taking safeguards. No one but a fool would go
on absorbing punishment if, by merely standing aside,
he could put an end to it. Deep Relaxation shows
how to step aside. It shows us how, when life grows
too intense, we can give frayed nerves a chance to
recover. At the same time Dynamic Breathing will
charge up our nervous batteries with fresh energy.
Once people realize their need of these stimulants,
only a little practice will be needed to give them all
they want through these channels.

Similarly, on the health front, we can keep stiff
old age much longer at bay if we practice Deep Contraction. For this is Nature's way of breaking up ad-
hesions and sending a reviving blood flush to stagnant
parts of the body. What about our mental condition-
ing? Dynamic Concentration is the most convenient
instrument for keeping the mind young and supple.

Of course, we've got to practice these techniques.
We have got to do them every day, however busy. And
the sooner we start them, the easier it will be for us.

Earlier in this book I reproduced Mass-Observation's independent report of what actual students

think of the Yogism method. Health magazines, too, have reported enthusiastically on the benefits. Naturally the health experts stress the physical improvements. I prefer Yogism to be judged as a way of expanding our realization of reality. Most of us could do with a wider perspective—we would be better citizens for it. Yet to be worth the having, this realization of a higher life must have a personal basis. It should not rest on vague theory. Microscopes, test tubes, and the statistical methods of modern science are limited windows to the world of real things, for they give access to physical sensations only. Philosophy, poetry, and the arts help more. But we should seek to widen our horizon by personal effort also. We need not fall down and worship any of these teachers. The *Yogabija Upanishad* warns us to beware of "the hundreds of forms of philosophy, or arguments, of scientific rules which entrap the true intellect in their nets and lead it astray from true knowledge." We should listen to that counsel today: it is more than ever needed.

Yes, personal effort is necessary. Yogism asks you to *do* something. You may well say, as have hundreds of others "But I am too busy—I haven't the time." Surely no one is so busy that he could not find fifteen or twenty minutes daily, with so much at stake? Health, after all, is fundamental to all other success. More and more it is being realized today that health depends, in the last analysis, on smooth coordination between mind and body. No longer does medicine confine its attention to purely physical factors. Doctors agree that to be really fit in your body, you need to be mentally well—and vice versa. Your inner drives and motivations matter just as much, if not more, than the spots or other symptoms of illness.

The study demands effort. It means shaking yourself out of complacency, making active preparations for a healthy, long life. It asks you to become aware of yourself as a person; to see things more objectively; to make actual adjustments; to redress lack of balance. That way, it says, you will become a more intelligent being. Until this necessary state of mental independence is achieved, people cannot help being envious, stupid, fearful, depressed, and irritated. The conditions are not symptomatic of evil but of a chaotic, inconsistent grasp of life.

I now make a bold statement. For every half-hour given daily to this four-way training, you can add a month to your life! Not just an extra month of senility, but a month of full, expressive, creative living! Every student of Yogism can add to his life by applying this daily routine. Already you have seen what better housing, sanitation and hygiene have done to increase the lifespan. The increase is such that insurance companies will soon be thinking seriously about revising their policies. For half the girls born today will live to be seventy-five years of age and half the boys to be seventy—these are the latest expectations of life, due to improved living conditions.

Tackle this problem of health in a direct, personal way and you may easily hit the century mark! Carry out regularly, every day, the Yogism four-way plan! Resolve now to live on happily and don't go looking for death when you encounter the seventies!

To an extent not yet appreciated, long life depends on activity of mind and body—which cuts out any idea of retiring when you are only sixty. The very last thing you need at sixty is rest, unless it happens that you are recovering from a serious sickness. *Carry on working, keep on the move, get proper daily periods of Deep Relaxation, keep your breathing apparatus sound by Dynamic Breathing, take a mind stretch and a muscle stretch every day through Dynamic Concentration and Deep Contraction.* At the age of seventy-one Professor Einstein started work on a new theory of the universe—whatever other parts of the Yogism long-life routine he missed, he was certainly helping himself by applying this one.

In ancient Rome the expectation of life was about twenty years. Today in the United States it is seventy-one-and-a-half for women and sixty-five for men, all through improvements in physical hygiene. With comparative effort on the mental plane, we could easily live a further quarter of a century. But we must cease leaving the initiative to "the doctor." None can help us to healthy long life so well as we can help ourselves.

Some may say, "I am already past middle age—I would have begun what you asked if I were younger, but now with my heart trouble, my arthritis, and these cold mornings, it is just too late!" No, despairing reader, it is never too late. Whatever your present age or state, the time to begin is *now!* If your bodily machine is defective, use it carefully, by all means. For mercy's sake, don't write it off!

Many an old crock of a car gives good service because it is intelligently driven. Drive you *your* vehicle according to this code! It will last you longer, take you further, and bear you, comfortably, through a happier world.

Summary of Techniques

STEP 1: DEEP RELAXATION

We will suppose you are now lying on your back on the floor—perhaps the floorboards feel hard, but that is better than a soft bed. Don't make the mistake of shifting every now and then to find a more easy position; having assumed a comfortable posture, with your weight fairly distributed, hold it. Movement should be checked—any change of position will upset what follows. Just try to distribute your weight evenly on the floor and resolve, come what may, to leave your weight and posture there, undisturbed.

Now stretch an arm, leg, or even your neck or feet—any part of the body. Stretch it hard, make the muscles contract, *and study what is happening.* (You'll be surprised at the way in which parts far removed from the seat of operations contract in sympathy. A strongly clenched fist, for example, will cause contractions to be felt all the way up your arm and down your shoulders and back.) Hold the stretch while you trace these sensations in detail, then let go. This completes Step 1.

Now, for your next step toward Deep Relaxation, stretch hard again—but this time, do it in slow motion. Build the stretch up slowly and observe and note every sensation inspired by it. Again, hold the stretch while you make a mental record of all that is happening. Then, once more in slow motion, let go. Here, now, is the secret of success; you must let go as slowly as possible, *carrying the "let-go" process beyond the point where you have ceased to be conscious of any physical sensation whatsoever.* Continue further with this "let-go" mechanism until you reach the stage where you are no longer *trying* to relax but have completely lost all feeling of alertness in the portions of your anatomy concerned.

It will be enough for your first attempts to direct your attention to one part of the body only. With repetition, your application of these principles should become more general, until you cease to think of specific areas and commence relaxing the whole body as a coordinated unit. From time to time, as you relax, you will become aware of muscle groups that have escaped attention or, having been relaxed at first, have again grown tense; they must be newly relaxed, of course. But remember not to make too much of an effort in your first attempts. Remember, too, that *any* success is worth accepting, however small— *any* relaxation is more beneficial than none.

After a time you will develop a definite sequence for Deep Relaxation—you will stop darting attention from this to that group of muscles. You will discover that it is best to begin with the head and then pass down the body, relaxing groups of muscles as you find them, easing the arms from the shoulders, the legs from the hips, and so on. But when you have completed this mental review and diminished the feeling of tension and alertness right down to the toes, you must turn back to the eyebrows, eyelids, and eyeballs. For these are the hardest parts of your anatomy to relax—this region which is, by proximity, most closely related to the organ of sight. There is almost sure to be some contraction here which normally escapes notice and needs relaxing a second or third time.

STEP 2: DEEP CONTRACTION

The Western student should confine himself to simple, natural, *impromptu* stretches of his own devising carried out while (1) sitting down, (2) while lying on the back, and (3) when in upright or standing posture. Henceforth, every day, stretch in each of these postures in turn *and give at least five minutes to the process.* Encourage your body to stretch slowly this way and that, holding each stretch for a minute or more if possible. Stretch your neck, chest, arms, back, and waist—let the movements be natural, smooth, and, above all, prolonged. During each stretch try to contract as many muscles as you can trace. Beware of sudden jerky movements—stretch slowly, gradually building up and, equally gradually, playing down the amount of energy and muscular tension involved.

Let us assume you have just finished a period of Deep Relaxation—the opposite state, in which all your body has been "at ease." You are lying on the floor, your feet outstretched, arms by sides, face upward. The Relaxation period has ended. Now, try lifting your left and right legs from the ground level. Do it very *slowly,* holding the legs stiff and pointing them straight out in line with the body. Immediately you will become conscious of a variety of contractions extending from the feet, up the calf, to the thighs, and still on upward to the abdominal region. Hold this stretch as long as possible; then *gently and slowly* lower the feet to the floor, in one smooth, controlled movement—and rest!

Now, sitting up on the floor, try to grasp your toes or

ankles with your left and right hands, bending down the trunk and keeping the legs well outstretched. Continue to bend as deeply as possible and hold the position for some time before gradually loosening your grip and returning, *slowly,* to the upright position.

Next lie in the horizontal position, this time with the face to the floor. Keep your legs straight out behind you and rest the hands on the floor in a line with the shoulders. Try now to elevate the body by pressing down on the hands. After some regular daily practice you will be able to lift the abdomen off the floor.

Finally, stretch in the standing position. This you might do by placing the hands on the thighs and, after expelling the breath, attempt to lift the abdomen, holding it up.

The foregoing stretching routines are suggestions only. Follow them if you wish—but also try stretches of your own devising. I repeat, *any* natural body stretch can be performed at this stage with immediate benefit, providing you stretch *slowly—deliberately . . . dynamically,* and hold it for as long as you can without straining. Spend five minutes or so on these Contraction exercises every morning, *after* your Deep Relaxation period. Or do them in the evening, if that is more convenient. Either period has its advantage.

STEP 3: DYNAMIC BREATHING

Dynamic Breathing involves a slow, sustained intake of air (via the nose). Simultaneously with this respiration, you learn to push out the abdominal area. (This enables you to fill the lower part of the lungs first. The pressure thus exerted on the abdominal wall has been found to stimulate organs concerned with digestion and elimination. After a week or two's practice, there will be a noticeable improvement in these latter functions.)

When the lungs have been slowly filled to capacity, the air is exhaled, *again through the nose*. This act of exhalation is also performed at a slow tempo.

Slow nasal inhalation and exhalation can be performed without risk or strain by all unaffected with lung disease. There is no need to hold the breath. One may even, if one choose, rest and breathe normally between two Dynamic Breaths. But if only five minutes or so be spent in the performance of this slow, sustained or, as I call it, Dynamic Breathing, first thing each morning and last thing each evening—it will soon improve vitality. For there is more involved in the principle of Dynamic Breathing than the simple physical operation of slowly inflating the lungs and, by the depth of respiration, massaging the abdominal area. I found that the mental suggestions that could be allied to this exercise were equally important.

Make your own first experiments in Dynamic Breathing as rhythmical and smooth as possible—that is to say, take approximately the same time to draw in the breath as to pass it out of the body. (Normally inhalation involves a shorter movement than exhalation, but you should strive to equalize them.) Aim at a regular rhythm. As you breathe in, *visualize* your limbs as hollow tubes, through which the health-giving *prana* is being drawn into your body. Picture this energy swelling all over your body, submerging your whole physique at the height of the inhalation. In the reverse action, exhale as slowly and in as controlled fashion as possible. Visualize the fatigue and exhaustion passing out of your system along with the expiring breath. You know that, physically, you are getting rid of poison—banish the fatigue and exhaustion with it.

Having indulged for some minutes in this highly dramatized breathing technique, finish with what we call the "Cleansing Breath." To do this you should again inhale slowly through the nose and, when you feel that your lungs are fully extended, expel the air suddenly— again through the nose. This time you exhale with a quick inward jerk of the abdomen. Do this cleansing breath two or three times (not more), and you will experience a "tonic" and bracing effect.

STEP 4: DYNAMIC CONCENTRATION

The formula is to focus your thought—all your thought—on one pinpoint, to begin with. It can, indeed, be quite literally the point of a pin: nothing better. Or, if you wish, the "target" may be the pattern of a handkerchief or the design of a small piece of wallpaper, or a single letter on a page or a symbol drawn on paper. It can be anything—the simpler, the better—but it must be *one definite object.*

Now, just for thirty seconds, focus your thought on this target, whatever its form. Not, mark you, on the impressions called up in your mind by simply "dwelling" on it. That kind of concentration is not one-pointed.

You may think thirty seconds is a short time for this exercise but when you practice it, the period will seem an eternity at first. Remember, you must nail down the whole thinking mechanism so that all your attention and all your imagination and all your consciousness are utterly, completely, monopolized by one thing. To begin with, this will prove quite impossible. But it is possible with practice, and so you must just try again—and again—until you have exhausted your mind.

Index